Ministry of Agriculture, Fisheries and Food

Food and Nutrient Intakes
of British Infants Aged
6-12 Months

London: HMSO

© Crown copyright 1992
Applications for reproduction should be made to HMSO
First published 1992

ISBN 0 11 242906 8

£12.50

Coventry University

Contents

- type of milk first given in a bottle/beaker
- age at introduction of solids
- age at introduction of solids and initial method of feeding
- age at introduction of solids by region
- choice of first foods used during weaning
- choice of second 'solid' food
- consumption of fluids other than milk and water

7. **Present feeding practices as reported in the interview**
- types of milks now used
- drinks most frequently consumed
- types of commercial infant food now consumed
- consumption of 'family foods' and recipe alterations
- removal of fat from meat
- addition of salt to foods
- addition of sugar to foods
- types of 'family foods' eaten
- use of vitamins or dietary supplements

8. **Quantities of foods consumed**
- infants aged 6–9 months and 9–12 months
- portion sizes of food groups and selected foods for infants aged 6–12 months

9. **Nutrient intake**
- introduction
- procedure for calculating nutrient intakes
- Dietary Reference Values (DRVs)
- summary of the nutrient intakes for infants aged 6–12 months and comparison with the RNIs
- variation with age
- variation between males and females
- energy
- contribution of protein, fat and carbohydrate to total energy intakes
- protein
- carbohydrate
- total sugars and individual sugars; non-milk extrinsic sugars and intrinsic sugars
- starch

- dietary fibre (Englyst i.e. non-starch polysaccharides)
- fat
- saturated fatty acids
- monounsaturated fatty acids
- polyunsaturated fatty acids
- cholesterol
- vitamin A (retinol and total carotenoids)
- vitamin D
- vitamin E
- vitamin C
- thiamin
- riboflavin
- niacin (niacin equivalents)
- folate
- vitamin B_6
- vitamin B_{12}
- pantothenic acid
- biotin
- minerals
- calcium
- iron
- zinc

References

Appendices

Authors' acknowledgements

We would like to thank everyone who contributed to the survey and the production of this report. We were supported by the staff at Research Surveys of Great Britain Limited who carried out the sampling, fieldwork, analysis of the questionnaire data and preliminary coding of the diaries and particular thanks are due to the interviewers who showed much commitment to a survey that placed considerable demands on their skills.

We would also like to record our gratitude to the following people for their support, technical advice and assistance at various stages of the survey;

- the Ministry of Agriculture, Fisheries and Food statisticians Mike Day, Gordon Farquharson and Josie Pearson (formerly of MAFF) and Janet Lewis and Helen Rose (formerly of Nutrition Branch of MAFF).

Most importantly, we would like to thank all those people who gave up so much of their time to take part in this survey, made the interviewers very welcome in their homes and showed such interest in the aims of the research.

List of Tables and Figures

Statistics

Tables showing percentages

Where percentages have been rounded to the nearest whole number they may not always add up to 100%.

Tables showing mean and median values

Values for means, medians, percentiles and standard deviations are shown to an appropriate number of decimal places.

Tests of significance

Tests for differences in population means used the t-test and the Mann-Whitney test.

Differences that are commented on in the text are shown as being significant at the 0.01, 0.025 and 0.05 levels. Differences that are not significant are those that were $p>0.05$.

Rounding of figures

In tables where figures have been rounded to the nearest final digit, there may be a discrepancy between the sum of the constituent items and the total shown.

Summary

In 1986 the Ministry of Agriculture, Fisheries and Food commissioned a national survey of the diets of British infants aged 6–12 months. The survey estimated the food and nutrient intake of this age group. The sample of 488 infants (81% response) was recruited in November 1986 from a nationally representative commercial baby panel (Research Surveys of Great Britain Ltd). The mothers completed a seven day quantitative diary record of all the food and drink consumed by their infant. Background and demographic information including past and present routine of milk and solids were obtained via a personal interview after the mother had completed the seven day diary record.

Initial feeding practices

The incidence of breastfeeding was 64%. The highest incidence of breastfeeding was amongst first time mothers with successively lower rates for higher birth orders.

Early introduction of solids was not uncommon. Sixteen per cent of mothers reported that their infant had received some solid food by eight weeks and this had increased to over 50% by 12 weeks of age. Almost all the infants in this survey had started mixed feeding by 24 weeks. Most mothers introduced cereals, rusks and commercial infant foods as the first weaning foods.

Food consumption

This survey provides an extensive database on the types and quantities of food fed to older infants and on the nutrients provided by these foods.

Infants aged 6–12 months consumed a wide range of foods with an increase in variety with increasing age. Whole cows milk was consumed by almost two thirds of infants aged 6–12 months. Infant formulas were consumed by 29% of infants. Overall, 7% of the infants received breast milk as their sole source of milk with a further 7% receiving breast milk in addition to other milks. Very few infants (5%) were receiving low fat milks as their main source of milk. Commercial infant foods formed an important part of the diet of most infants with few relying on 'family foods' alone. Commercial infant foods were less important in the diet of the 9–12 month old infant than in the younger age group. In the younger infants (6–9 months), 'family foods' that were consumed by over half the infants during the seven day record included breakfast cereals, bread and fat spreads, biscuits and cakes, cows milk, meat dishes, potatoes, vegetables and fruit. Among infants aged 9–12 months more than three quarters of the sample consumed these foods. In the older group, yogurt was a popular food being consumed by over half the sample. Besides milks and other drinks, yogurt was the food that was consumed in the largest quantity. Chocolate confectionery and crisps (including savoury snacks), although not consumed in large amounts, were consumed by over half and one third of the older infants respectively during the seven day period. Over one third of mothers altered family recipes specifically for the infant, mainly by avoiding the addition of salt and spices and to a lesser extent sugar.

Nutrient intakes

Nutrient and energy intakes were compared with the UK Dietary Reference Values. However caution is required in the interpretation of the results as a seven day dietary record may not be sufficient to adequately assess intake of some nutrients. Besides zinc (90% of the Reference Nutrient Intake (RNI)) and vitamin D (50% of the RNI), average intakes of nutrients from food were well above the RNIs. However the median iron intake was 7mg which corresponds to 90% of the RNI. Supplements provided additional vitamin D in 43% of the sample which enabled these infants to meet the RNI (further vitamin D will also be provided by sunlight).

Fat provided 37% of energy, which is lower than was recorded for older British children and adults. Approximately 60% (59%) of total fat was provided by milks (including infant formulas and breast milk) and dairy products. Milks continued to be important sources of other nutrients providing over 40% of protein and energy and over half the average intake of calcium, riboflavin and iodine. Those infants whose predominant type of milk was cows milk, breast milk or low fat milk had significantly ($p<0.01$) lower iron intakes than those whose main milk was infant formula.

Although the mean intake of iron was 8.1mg (104% of the RNI), the median intake of 7mg was below the RNI of 7.8mg and 15% of infants had iron intakes below the LRNI. Average intakes of iron were lower in older infants (mean 6.7mg, median 5.8mg) than the younger infants (mean 9.3mg, median 8.8mg). Commercial infant foods were a major source of iron for most infants. In the small number of infants (18%) who were 'reported to not consume any commercial infant food', the mean iron intake was 62% of the RNI. Less than one sixth of the iron in the diets of infants fed predominantly 'family food' was from meat and fish dishes. Thus the majority of the iron was non-haem iron.

Protein provided 14% and carbohydrate 49% of energy for infants aged 6–12 months. Non-milk extrinsic sugars (NMES), provided 9% and 12% of energy for infants aged 6–9 months and 9–12 months respectively. Infant fruit juices (including fruit drinks) and squashes were the main source of NMES.

On average, vitamin C intakes were four times the RNI. Over 60% of total vitamin C was provided by commercial infant foods, many of which have a high level of fortification.

This survey suggests that on average the diets of British infants aged 6–12 months are nutritionally adequate. However, iron intakes may be marginal particularly in the older infants, in those infants fed largely on 'family foods' and in those who consumed cows milk, breast milk or low fat milks as their main milk. Zinc intakes also tended to be lower than the RNI.

The findings of this survey have been passed to the COMA Sub-Committee on the Weaning Diet for their consideration.

1 Background and purpose of the survey

The need for the survey

The Ministry of Agriculture, Fisheries and Food (MAFF) aims to ensure that an adequate, safe and varied food supply is available at all times from which consumers can choose, with confidence, a healthy and enjoyable diet. In order to do this, information is required on both average and extreme food consumption patterns to identify and anticipate inadequate or inappropriate food and nutrient intakes. These data can then be used for future policy discussion and formulation. Continuous monitoring of the intakes of foods and nutrients in the diet takes place at a national level by means of the National Food Survey and ad hoc surveys among particular sections of the UK population. At the time of the study little quantitative information was available on the range of foods that may be fed to infants, or the nutrient intake of older infants.

Infant feeding practices vary over time due to such factors as social changes, changes in attitudes and in the types of commercial infant foods available (Whitehead and Paul, 1987). During early infancy most infants are dependent on human milk or infant formulas for nearly all their nutritional needs. During weaning, milk feeds are gradually supplemented by semi-solid food. The age at which weaning starts and the form that weaning takes can vary considerably. Infants may be fed on modified 'family foods' and/or commercial infant foods in addition to breast milk, infant formulas, 'follow-on' milk or unmodified whole cows milk. The Panel on Child Nutrition of the Committee on Aspects of Food Policy recommends that the majority of infants should be offered a mixed diet not later than six months (DHSS, 1988). Few national data are available on the food and nutrient intakes of older infants in Britain or the range of these intakes. Little is known about the relative nutritional importance of commercial infant foods and 'family foods'. To elicit this information and to determine differences by region, socio-economic groups and presence of other children in the family, the Nutrition Branch of the Ministry of Agriculture, Fisheries and Food (MAFF) commissioned Research Surveys of Great Britain (RSGB) Limited to perform a dietary survey of infants aged 6–12 months. This survey also provides a resource for estimating intakes of non-nutrients such as food additives and contaminants.

1

The aims of the study

The survey aimed to:

1. determine the type and quantities of food eaten by infants and the extent of variation between individuals according to such factors as the infant's age and the family's socioeconomic background;

2. estimate the nutrient intake of infants;

3. determine the relative importance of 'family foods' and commercial infant foods; and

4. investigate the extent of addition of salt and sugar to foods specifically prepared for the infant.

2 | Survey methodology

Recruitment of the sample

To meet the aims of the survey a large national sample of infants aged 6–12 months old was required. Recruitment of the sample and field work was carried out by a market research company. Research Surveys of Great Britain Limited was chosen because of their expertise in the area having already established a panel of over 1800 mothers of infants aged up to two years. This market research panel is designed to be nationally representative with regards to geographical location, social class, age and birth order for children under two years in Great Britain. However, one parent families and ethnic minorities may be under-represented on the panel.

Outline of the survey design in order to meet the aims of the survey

Mothers of infants on the panel routinely keep fortnightly records of all items purchased for their infants. For this survey, all mothers of infants aged 6–12 months were asked to keep a quantitative record of all food consumed by their infant over a seven day period. Food intake was monitored at a time when mothers were not completing the normal purchase diary.

In order to identify the type, method of preparation and quantity of foods and drinks consumed by the infants a dual approach was adopted. Firstly the mother of each infant completed a seven day diary quantifying all the food and drink consumed by her infant. After completion of the diary, further information on the family, such as presence of other children, and also information on the way their infant was fed prior to the survey, was obtained via a personal interview of the mother.

Choice of method of data collection

A diary which was structured into separate sections for recording specific food items was chosen as the most suitable method for recording what the infant ate and drank. A structured recall interview, which depends on the mother being able to remember, at the time of interview, and with judicious prompting, everything that the baby had eaten or drunk over a fixed period, was considered inappropriate in view of the need for accuracy, particularly for the measurement of amounts consumed.

Duration of the recording period

Two alternative durations for the food record (seven days and three days) were considered. A three day record has advantages for the mother as it is likely to be less onerous. However it would have required a randomised start date. It also requires a larger sample to achieve the same level of precision for average food intake of infants. Furthermore, eating patterns at weekends may vary from the usual week day routine, so a seven day diary covering a weekend was chosen. Keeping a food record for an entire week also allows for a simpler sampling procedure and reduces the impact of unusual circumstances, such as illness or days away from home, on recorded intake.

Design of the food diary

Each diary contained a set of seven pages, one specified for each day of the week. The diary was divided into four sections (commercial infant foods, milk drinks, other drinks and 'family foods') which allowed information specific to each food type to be collected, for example whether sugar was added to yogurt, bread was toasted, meat was casseroled, roasted or prepared in some other way.

Recording procedure

Foods were not weighed directly; however accurate measurement of amounts of food actually eaten was important, and a standard scoop and measuring jug were issued to all mothers in order to ensure that amounts were recorded in the same units (scoops and fractions thereof, millilitres or fluid ounces). There were certain sections of the diary that offered the alternative of recording the quantity consumed in 'units' (e.g. numbers of biscuits) for which a standard weight could be assumed. In addition, some items such as cartons of yogurt or cans and jars of commercial infant food were recorded in terms of the pack size and the proportion of it consumed. The dry and liquid component of a meal, e.g. instant savoury meals and water, were measured separately. This approach ensured that appropriate nutrient composition factors were applied to foods of different consistency. It was anticipated that bananas would be fed to infants quite frequently and that the description of their size could vary quite markedly between individuals. In order to try and standardise the description, mothers were issued with a 'banana measuring guide' (Appendix I). This gave templates of a typical small, medium and large banana in their skin with a range of length measurements which corresponded to each descriptive category.

This method was chosen because it provided sufficiently accurate quantification of most foods for the purpose of the survey and was considered to be less demanding than weighing foods. The structured food diary enabled information to be collected in sufficient detail to allow appropriate coding for nutritional evaluation.

3 Pilot survey

Pilot survey

A small scale pilot survey was conducted in order to test the suitability of the data collection methods and to assess whether it was feasible for the mother to record the information in the detail required. It also enabled the suitability of the diary structure to be assessed and to provide possible answers to questions in the interview which could then be precoded.

The pilot survey was conducted between 16 June and 1 July 1986. Four sampling points (Aldershot, Basingstoke, Southall and Walthamstow) were chosen. Five infants from each sampling point were selected for the survey of which a net sample of seventeen was achieved. This represents a participation rate of 85%.

After completion of the diary and interview, the interviewer identified problems that mothers had with the diaries which were not obvious from the completed records. Where possible these were resolved for the main stage study.

Post pilot survey

Following the pilot study, mothers of Panel infants aged 6–12 months were asked whether if approached, they would be willing to participate in a similar study. The results suggested that the required sample size could be achieved from the Panel.

4 | Main survey

Collection of data

Interviewers were each instructed to recruit up to six mothers of infants born between 25 October 1985 and 24 April 1986 at the normal placement of Baby Panel materials, on 2–4 November 1986. Each mother was asked to complete the diary over any seven consecutive days during the following two weeks, though preferably starting the day after placement, whilst the requirements were still fresh in her mind. The mothers were issued with a standard jug and scoop, a revised booklet of instructions, a 'banana measuring guide' and a revised seven day diary set (Appendices I and II). The interviewer described the general procedure of recording everything the infant ate, whether at home or not, and stressed the need for accuracy and completeness. To illustrate how to complete the record, mothers were asked to recall the foods consumed by her infant on the previous day. This was recorded as an example page by the interviewer, showing the detail required. This information was not coded for analysis.

It was recognised that infants often do not consume all the food or drink offered to them. Interviewers therefore stressed the need to record what was actually eaten rather than the amount offered. In certain sections of the diary an additional column was left for 'amount eaten'.

Discrete items of food which were left or, for example, dropped could be quantified relatively easily and recorded. However infants are often messy eaters with food smeared on the face, hands and bibs. This wastage is difficult to quantify but is likely to be greatest at the beginning of the weaning process and again when infants start to feed themselves with a spoon. For most infants in the survey weaning was well established. Less than 20% of the sample were able to feed themselves with a spoon. We concluded that for most infants the non-quantified food on hands, faces and bibs etc was likely to be nutritionally insignificant. Therefore, no further deductions have been made.

Diaries were collected by the interviewer between 16–18 November 1986. They were checked by the interviewer for completeness and the mother was asked to raise any queries. If there were any outstanding problems or if unusual circumstances were involved, a note was made on the back of the relevant diary page.

The interview (Appendix III) was conducted after the diary had been checked so as not to influence 'normal' feeding practice such as usage of salt and sugar. This explored aspects of each infant's past and present diet and possible influences upon it. The panel 'sign up card' (Appendix IV), available for all respondents, provided much of the demographic and socioeconomic data required. The questionnaire therefore concentrated on gathering information on the infant's general dietary practices.

This included:

- preparation of foods specifically for the infant, the addition of salt and sugar, the removal of fat;

- additional information to supplement that given in the diaries such as dilution of drinks, thickness of slices of bread, the type of fat spread normally used and whether crusts were eaten or not. Mothers were asked about the range of foods fed to their infant in order to cover those items that may not have been consumed during the recording week;

- past and present routine of milk and solids feeding such as the incidence of breast and bottle feeding both at present and at birth, the number of milk feeds per day, consumption of drinks besides milk and types of solid foods introduced initially and subsequently;

- additional background and demographic information such as the infant's reported weight and stage of physical activity, presence of other children, allergies and major illnesses and mother's working status and educational achievement.

Due to the time consuming nature of the respondent's task, an incentive in the form of a commemorative coin was given to the mother of each infant who took part in the survey.

Coding and editing the information obtained during the interview and food record

Extensive coding of diary information was required in order to analyse the nutrient content of an individual's food intake. Food items were designated codes covering not only the item itself but also details on, for example, addition of sugar and milk, dilution and inclusion of vegetables in meat dishes recorded in the diary and for commercial infant foods whether canned or not. The code list consisted of over one thousand food codes. The amount of food eaten on each occasion was also coded.

Mothers recorded the amounts of food or drink consumed in a number of ways, so a detailed conversion task was therefore necessary. Liquids recorded in fluid ounces were converted to millilitres using a conversion chart. Nutritionists at MAFF weighed samples of other foods in order to give a typical scoop weight for a specific item, and, where applicable, a weight per unit. These weights were included on the code list. Where insufficient details were provided or a food did not fit one of the standard categories, judgements about coding were made by qualified nutritionists. When only a proportion of a made up food was consumed, calculations of the actual quantities of the dried food and liquid were made and coded appropriately. Breast milk was difficult to quantify as test weighing was impractical but it was felt that it should not be ignored. 'Amounts' of breast milk were coded as the number of minutes of feeding which were later converted to volumes (for a more detailed explanation see Appendix V). To simplify the recording of information on bread and the type and quantity of spread used, information on 'usual practice' for each infant was collected in the questionnaire. This included whether the bread was usually from a sliced or unsliced loaf, the thickness of each slice, whether crusts were removed and the type of fat spread most frequently used for the infant. This, together with details recorded in the diary, was used to quantify bread and spread consumption for each infant.

An edit check was made on all the diary data using acceptable maximum amounts thought likely to be fed to an infant in any one day. All diaries failing for any reason were inspected by the nutritionists. Following completion of these checks the information from the diary record was linked to the nutrient databank (Appendix VII) and the nutrients provided by the foods were then calculated.

5 Response to the survey and characteristics of the interviewed sample

Sample

Of the 600 mothers who had infants of the required age, 488 were willing and able to take part. This represents a response rate of 81%. There was a greater proportion of female (54%) than male (46%) infants. There were three sets of twins.

Age

To describe the current practices as reported at the interview, infants were divided into 3 age groups (Table 5.1).

Table 5.1 Age of infants

Age (weeks)	Number	Percentage of total
23–36	192	39
37–42	122	25
43–54	174	36

However, for comparisons of nutrient intakes to the Dietary Reference Values (DRVs) (DH, 1991) infants were regrouped into two age groups (Table 5.2).

Table 5.2 Age of infants by sex

Age (months)	Number	Male	Female
6–<9*	258	130	128
9–12	230	96	134

*Hereafter 6–<9 months referred to as 6–9 months.

Although 15 of the recruited infants were outside the 6–12 month age range (four aged 23–26 weeks, 11 aged 53–54 weeks) they have not been excluded from the analyses.

Region

For analysis of the information obtained from the questionnaire, the data were classified into five regions (Table 5.3). For analysis of the nutritional data the regions were reclassified into three groups, Scotland and Northern England; Wales, Midlands and South West (SW); and South East (SE), East Anglia and London (Table 5.4).

There were no significant differences in age between the three regional groups.

Table 5.3   Age (weeks) of infants by region

	Number	Mean age (weeks)
Scotland	47	37
Northern England*	131	39
Midlands and East Anglia	112	40
Wales and SW England	60	41
South East and London	138	39

*Northern England refers to North East England, North West England, Yorkshire and Humberside

Table 5.4   Age of infants by regional groups

	Age in weeks			
	Number	Mean	Median	SD
Scotland and Northern England	178	38.9	38	8.2
Wales, Midlands and South West	149	40.2	41	7.2
South East, East Anglia and London	161	38.8	38	7.9

Socioeconomic group

The socioeconomic breakdown used for this survey was based on the occupation of the head of household. For nutritional analyses, the sample was split into two socioeconomic groups, ABC1 and C2DE, and further subdivided by age (Table 5.6).

Table 5.5   Socioeconomic group of infants (per cent)

Socioeconomic group	Percentage of total
AB	12
C1	22
C2	39
DE	27

Table 5.6   Socioeconomic group by age of infant

	6–9 months (%)	9–12 months (%)
ABC1	91 (35%)	72 (31%)
C2DE	167 (65%)	158 (69%)

Employment of the mother

At the time of the survey 21% of the mothers were in paid employment, largely on a part-time basis (19% of the sample).

Family size

The General Household Survey (GHS) in 1986 estimated that 1.5% of households with a child aged 0–4 years were single parent families (OPCS, 1989). In this survey four infants (0.8% of the sample) were from single parent families.

Table 5.7 Household composition

Number in household*	Percentage of total
2	1
3	28
4	40
5	19
6	9
7	2
8	2

*number including the mother and study infant

Age of mother

Although the age of the mother when the study infant was born was very variable, the majority were in their late 20's and early 30's. For one third of the mothers the 'study infant' was her first child.

Table 5.8 Age of mother at infant's birth

Age (years)	Percentage
15–17	1
18–19	5
20–21	8
22–24	18
25–27	22
28–30	23
31+	24

Level of education of the mother

Table 5.9 Age when mother completed full time education

Age (years)	Percentage
< 16	24
16–17	54
18–19	11
20–22	8
23+	3

Fewer than one quarter of the mothers (22%) had received higher education.

Country of origin of the mother

Table 5.10 Country of origin of mother

Country	%	GHS %
Britain (England, Scotland and Wales)	96	95
Ireland	1	
Pakistan/India	1	3
West Indies and Africa	1	1
Other	2	1

Comparison with the GHS data (OPCS, 1989) suggests that ethnic minorities may be slightly underrepresented.

6 INITIAL FEEDING PRACTICES AS DETERMINED AT THE INTERVIEW

Incidence of breastfeeding

The incidence of breastfeeding for this survey is defined as the proportion of babies who received some breast milk during the first week or two of life. More than half the mothers (55%) reported that they solely breastfed their child in the first week or two after birth, whereas 36% were bottlefed only. Nine per cent of the infants were fed by combination of breast and bottle. Therefore, overall 64% received some breast milk.

Table 6.1   Incidence of breastfeeding by region (per cent)

Region	Incidence of breastfeeding* %	Incidence of exclusive breastfeeding %
Scotland	55	51
Northern England	57	43
Midlands, E Anglia	60	48
Wales and SW England	63	58
South East and London	77	70

*Some infants received infant formulas in addition to breast milk.

The incidence of breastfeeding in London and the South East was significantly greater than in Scotland ($p < 0.01$), Northern England ($p < 0.01$) and the Midlands and East Anglia ($p < 0.05$). These trends were shown by earlier Department of Health (DH)/Office of Population Censuses and Surveys (OPCS) national studies (Martin and Monk, 1982; Martin and White, 1988). The incidence of breastfeeding is still considerably lower than in many other countries; for example in Canada the incidence was 75% (McNally et al, 1985) and in Norway 95% of the mothers reported breastfeeding initially (Kjaernes, 1988).

Incidence of breastfeeding by birth order

Table 6.2   Incidence of breastfeeding by birth order (per cent)

Birth order	Number	Percentage of sample	Incidence of breastfeeding %	Exclusively breastfed %
First baby	164	34	71	59
Second baby	195	40	66	56
Third baby	87	18	49	44
Fourth or more	42	9	57	52

Breastfeeding declined with increasing birth order and this difference reached statistical significance ($p < 0.01$).

Incidence of breastfeeding by socioeconomic group

Table 6.3   Incidence of breastfeeding by socioeconomic group

Socioeconomic group	Incidence of breastfeeding %
AB	81
C1	78
C2	65
DE	44

There was a significant difference (p<0.01) in the incidence of breastfeeding by socioeconomic group.

Duration of breastfeeding

The duration of breastfeeding was very variable with 14% of infants continuing to receive some breast milk after six months of age. Amongst those who had breastfed initially but who had now ceased, the mean duration was 14 weeks (SD 11.9, median 10 weeks). Twenty-three per cent of mothers who breastfed had stopped before four weeks and this had increased to 47% by six weeks. This compares with 39% in the 1985 DH/OPCS survey (Martin and White, 1988). This may be a real difference between the two samples or may reflect differences in the design of the two surveys. In our survey, mothers were recruited when their infants were between 6–12 months old and asked to recall the duration of different feeding practices. Although mothers are likely to be able to recall whether, for example they breastfed or not, they may not be able to recall precisely for how many weeks they continued.

Table 6.4   Duration of breastfeeding

Duration (weeks)	Number	Percentage of the sample who ceased breastfeeding	Cumulative per cent
1–3	53	22.5	22.5
4–8	58	24.6	47.1
9–12	24	10.2	57.3
13–16	19	8.0	65.3
17–20	14	5.9	71.2
21–24	19	8.0	79.2
25–28	14	5.9	85.1
29–32	15	6.4	91.5
33–36	9	3.8	95.3
37–40	7	3.0	98.3
41–44	3	1.3	99.6
47	1	0.4	100
Total	**236**		

Type of milk first given in a bottle

Each mother was asked what type of milk was given initially to her infant from a beaker or a bottle. The response is presented in Table 6.5.

Table 6.5   First type of milk from a bottle/beaker

Milk	Number	Percentage of total†
Infant formula		
Whey dominant		
Aptamil	7	1.5
Cow and Gate Premium	136	30.0
Farley's Osterfeed*	19	4.2
SMA Gold Cap	158	34.9
Casein dominant		
Cow and Gate Plus	27	6.0
Milumil	17	3.8
Farley's Ostermilk No. 2*	1	0.2
Farley's Ostermilk Complete Formula*	5	1.1
SMA White Cap	23	5.1
Soya-based		
Cow and Gate Formula S	1	0.2
Wysoy	4	0.9
Other	4	0.9
Follow-on formulas		
Progress	1	0.2
Cows milk		
Whole	47	10.4
Semi-skimmed	2	0.4
Soya milk	1	0.2

*Farley's have since altered the names and formulation of their products.
†Excludes infants continuing to receive breast milk as sole milk.

Age at introduction of solids

The age at which 'solid foods' were introduced into the infant's diet was very variable and ranged from a minimum of three weeks to a maximum of 32 weeks with no statistical difference between males (mean 13.2 weeks, SD 4.7) and females (mean 13.5 weeks, SD 4.6). On average, infants received solids by 13 weeks of age. In three cases some solid food had been consumed as early as three weeks. By eight weeks 16% of the infants had received some solid food; this had increased to over 50% at 12 weeks of age. Weaning had started for almost all (99%) the infants by 24 weeks. Infants who were initially solely breastfed were on average given solid food later (14.1 weeks, SD 4.4) than those who received either both breast and bottle

Table 6.6   Age (weeks) at introduction of solids by sex

		Number	Mean age	SD
Entire sample		488	13.3	4.6
Males		226	13.2	4.7
Males,	breast	119	13.6	4.7
	bottle	85	12.8	4.6
	breast and bottle	22	12.0	5.2
Females		262	13.5	4.6
Females,	breast	148	14.5	4.2
	bottle	91	12.0	5.1
	breast and bottle	23	13.0	3.6

(12.6 weeks, SD 4.4) or bottle milk only (12.4 weeks, SD 4.8). Although bottlefed infants were on average given solid food earlier, the differences found in this survey were not so marked as in other reports (Whitehead et al., 1986 and Wilkinson and Davies, 1978).

Age at introduction of solids (weeks) by region

There was regional variation in the ages when solid foods were first introduced. Solids tended to be introduced slightly later in the SE and London especially in comparison with Northern England. This difference may reflect the higher incidence of breastfeeding in the South.

Table 6.7   Age (weeks) at introduction of solids by region

Region	Number	Mean age	SD
Scotland	47	13.0	5.0
Northern England	131	12.0	4.1
Midlands and E Anglia	112	13.5	4.9
Wales and SW England	60	13.9	4.4
South East and London	138	14.3	4.7

The advice from the Committee on the Medical Aspects of Food Policy (COMA), covering infant feeding practices (Present day practices in infant feeding: third report, DHSS, 1988) is that very few infants will require solid food before the age of three months but the vast majority should be offered a mixed diet not later than the age of six months. In our survey, early introduction of solids was common. Similar results were found in the 1985 DH/OPCS survey (Martin and White, 1988) where over half had been given solids by the time they were three months old. Although the practice of early introduction to solids was considerably lower than in the 1970's (Martin, 1978), it is clear that many mothers are starting solids earlier than is generally advised.

Choice of first foods used during weaning

Cereals were the most common weaning foods, with 88% of the infants consuming them as their first solid food. Baby rice was the most popular (56%) followed by rusks and granulated rusks (24%) and other cereals (8%). The majority of mothers mixed the cereal with a small quantity of liquid, mainly infant formulas or water and then fed it from a spoon. However 16 infants were given baby cereals incorporated into a large quantity of either infant formula, cows milk or water which were then given from the bottle. The infants receiving cereals in this way were not necessarily given solids at an early age. Only 5% of mothers prepared fruit or vegetable purees as first foods and these tended to be given to infants who were introduced to solids relatively later than average (mean 17.6 weeks, SD 4.7), compared with those given commercial infant cereals and rusks (mean 12.9 weeks, SD 4.4) or other commercial infant foods, e.g. stage I savouries (mean 14.9 weeks, SD 5.2).

15

Choice of second 'solid' food

Instant and strained stage I* savoury meals were the most common second solid food, introduced to 34% of the infants. A further 20% were given baby rice and other baby cereals, 19% rusks and granulated rusks and 9% were given stage I puddings or yoghurts designed specifically for infants. The remainder were offered 'family foods' such as banana (4%) and other pureed fruit (6%), pureed vegetables (5%), egg (1%) and bread (0.4%).

Reported consumption of fluids other than milk and water

In this survey 44% of infants consumed 'baby syrups' as their first alternative drink to milk and water. Baby syrups have since been withdrawn and they have been replaced in the market by concentrated fruit juice drinks. One fifth of the sample drank concentrated powder drinks flavoured with, for example, fennel, hibiscus and rosehip which are made up with water. Other initial drinks included 'baby' fruit juice (20%), other pure fruit juice drinks (7%) and fruit squash (4%).

The age at introduction of these drinks was again very variable ranging from one week to 40 weeks, the mean was 13 weeks (SD 8.1) and the median was 12 weeks. As with the introduction of solid food, mothers in Scotland and Northern England reported introducing non-milk drinks at a slightly earlier age (mean 11–12 weeks compared with 14 weeks in the remainder of Britain).

---

*Infant foods were categorised according to the manufacturers' description, e.g. Stage I, Stage II.

7 Feeding practices at the time of the seven day food record

The following results are presented as a percentage of the total number of infants participating in the study. In addition, the infants have been assigned to one of three groups according to their age at the time of study. Feeding practices will vary with, amongst other things, the age of the infant and will depend on what stage of the weaning process (mixed feeding) has been reached.

Table 7.1 Proportion of infants by age group

Age group	1	2	3
Age (weeks)	23–36	37–42	43–54
Number	192	122	174
Percentage	39	25	36

Types of milks reported to be currently used

Cows milk was the most popular milk being consumed by almost two thirds of infants aged 6–12 months. Overall, 7% of infants were still receiving breast milk as their sole source of milk; 71% of these were in the youngest group. A further 7% of all the infants received breast milk in addition to other milks.

Formula milks were fed to 29% of the infants, SMA Gold Cap (Wyeth) remaining the most popular brand overall, although Plus (Cow and Gate) was the major brand amongst the older infants. Soya formula milk was fed to 2% of infants. Progress (Wyeth), a follow-on milk, was consumed by six infants (1%). Half the mothers reported that they had changed milks at some time.

Table 7.2 Types of milk reported to be currently used by age group

Age group	1 %	2 %	3 %	Total %
Formula milk excluding soya	48	24	14	30
Soya formula milk	4	2	0.5	2
Follow-on milk	1	2	0.5	1
Cows milk	39	71	87	64
Breast milk	13	4	3	7

Percentages exceed 100% where more than one type of milk was used.

Although the majority of cows milk consumers were given whole milk, 5% received some semi-skimmed milk with less than 1% of the sample fed some fully skimmed milk. Similar percentages were found in the DH/OPCS 1985 Infant Feeding Study (Martin and White, 1988) where 7% of infants at 9–12 months were receiving low fat milks. The Panel on Child Nutrition of the Committee on Medical Aspects of Food Policy (DHSS, 1988) recommends that these low fat milks are not suitable for children up to five years and that semi-skimmed milk should be given to children over two years only in certain circumstances, for example, where semi-skimmed milk is the type of milk used by the rest of the family and the intake of energy and fat soluble vitamins is adequate from other sources.

Other drinks

Mothers were asked what kind of drink her infant had most often nowadays (Table 7.3). Three per cent of the infants had never been offered drinks other than milk and water. A large proportion of the younger infants consumed drinks designed specifically for babies with baby syrups being the most popular. The older infants (group 3) consumed baby syrups and baby juices and more consumed tea (13%) and fruit squash (26%) as their usual drink. Overall fruit squash was the most popular alternative drink to milk and water and was consumed by 19% of the infants.

Table 7.3   Types of drinks (excluding milks) reported to be consumed most frequently

Age group	1 %	2 %	3 %	Total %
Milky drinks	3	2	2	2
Baby syrup	25	13	9	16
Baby fruit juice	13	8	6	9
Baby fruit juice concentrate	13	16	6	11
Fruit juice	11	17	16	14
Infant powdered drink	8	6	6	7
Fruit squash	12	19	26	19
Water	4	4	3	3
Tea	5	9	13	9

Types of commercial infant food reported to be currently consumed

In this study 82% of the infants were fed some commercial infant food. Those who were given solely 'family foods'* tended to be the older infants with an average age of 44 weeks.

*'Family Foods' refers to all foods other than commercially prepared infant foods.

Table 7.4 Proportion of infants consuming different types of commercial infant food by age group

Age group	1 %	2 %	3 %	Total %
Stage I savoury	40	18	12	25
Stage I puddings*	42	21	11	26
Stage II savoury	42	46	45	44
Stage II puddings*	38	46	31	37
Instant savoury	33	15	6	19
Instant puddings*	28	11	10	17
Baby cereals	44	22	9	26
Baby yogurt	29	25	11	22
Rusks	64	45	33	48
No special baby food	6	20	31	18

*Puddings includes fruit based desserts and fruit purees.

As expected consumption of stage I and instant savoury meals and desserts declined with increasing age as did consumption of baby cereals and baby yogurt. The popularity of stage II savoury meals in each of the three age groups was remarkably similar although there was an increasing number of infants consuming only 'family food'.

Consumption of 'family foods' and recipe alterations

Almost all the infants (92%) between 6 and 12 months were fed some 'family foods'. Three per cent of all infants ate completely different recipes to those which were prepared for the rest of the family, whereas 32% of mothers used similar recipes but modified them by omitting certain ingredients.

Table 7.5 Proportion consuming modified 'family foods' by age group

Age group	1 %	2 %	3 %	Total %
As rest of family	46	63	67	58
Modified ingredients	35	31	28	32
Different recipes	4	0	4	3
No 'family food'	14	6	2	8

Those mothers who modified or used different recipes were then asked in what way they varied the food given to their infant.

Table 7.6 Type of recipe alterations by age group

Age group	1 %	2 %	3 %	Total %
No salt	35	23	25	28
No sugar	18	10	10	13
No spices	23	17	20	20
Leave out, strain fat	3	1	2	2
Other	1	2	2	1

Recipe alterations were most common amongst mothers of younger infants (group 1).

Removal of fat from meat

Mothers were later asked specifically about the removal of fat from meat and the addition of salt and sugar to certain food items which were then fed to their infant.

Table 7.7   Removal of fat from meat

	Number of consumers of selected foods	Fat removed (% of consumers)
Bacon and ham	133	68
Meat, roast and grilled	319	64
Mince, dishes made with mince	348	43
Poultry dishes and casseroles	275	56

More than 50% of mothers who cooked meat for their infants claimed to remove the fat before giving it to them. Amongst bacon and ham consumers 68% had the fat removed.

Addition of salt to foods consumed

Table 7.8   Addition of salt to selected foods

Food	Number of consumers of selected foods	Salt added (% of consumers)
Potatoes	433	39
Vegetables excluding potatoes	434	36
Meat, roast and grilled	319	10
Mince, dishes made with mince	348	22
Offal e.g. liver and liver dishes	165	13
Other meat dishes and casseroles excluding offal	318	24
Rice, pasta	225	18
Fish and fish dishes	295	13
Egg dishes (egg yolk, egg white)	318	12

Salt was mainly added to potatoes, vegetables, meat dishes and meat casseroles. Of those infants who consumed potatoes and vegetables, 39% and 36% of mothers respectively added salt to them. The COMA report on Infant Feeding (DHSS, 1988) states that moderation should be exercised in the consumption of common salt at all ages.

Addition of sugars to foods consumed

Table 7.9   Addition of sugar to selected foods

	Number of consumers of selected foods	Addition of sugar (% of consumers)
Breakfast cereals	355	33
Fruit (fresh, stewed)	389	22
Milk based desserts	370	45

One third of the infants who consumed breakfast cereals had sugar added to them in the home, whilst 45% of mothers who gave their infant milk based dishes sweetened them with sugar. The COMA report on Infant Feeding (DHSS, 1988) suggests that the regulation of sugar consumption is desirable so as to reduce the risk of dental caries and the possibility of obesity.

Types of 'family foods' eaten

Infants aged 6–12 months consumed a very wide range of foods, with an increase in variety as expected, with increasing age. A summary of the types of 'family foods' consumed by infants in each age group and overall is presented in Table 7.10.

Table 7.10 Proportion of infants reported to be consuming selected foods by age

Age group	1 %	2 %	3 %	Total %
Biscuits	46	81	89	70
Breakfast cereals	57	78	87	73
Bread/toast	76	93	99	89
Potato crisps	11	21	46	26
Sweets/chocolates	43	68	78	62
Yogurt (not baby)	47	70	72	62
Fresh/stewed fruit	71	84	86	80
Potatoes	83	93	97	91
Other vegetables	81	91	97	89
Rice/pasta	26	52	64	46
Bacon and ham	12	25	45	27
Meat and poultry	48	72	79	65
Mince, mince dishes	59	73	84	71
Other meat dishes	50	72	77	65
Poultry dishes	47	57	67	57
Liver, liver dishes	23	36	44	34
Fish, fish dishes	44	67	74	60
Egg yolk	56	66	64	61
Egg white	38	53	55	48
Whole egg dishes	51	74	75	65
Cheese, cheese dishes	46	70	76	63
Milk based dishes	62	84	84	76
Other puddings	28	61	56	46
None of these	4	1	0	2

Over 80% of the infants consumed basic foods such as bread (89%), fruit (80%), potatoes (91%), and vegetables (89%). Mince was the most popular form of meat (71%), whereas only 27% ate bacon and ham and 34% liver and liver dishes. Fish and fish dishes were consumed by 60% of all the infants and 74% of the older infants. Egg yolk was more popular than egg white with 61% and 48% of the infants eating them respectively. Forty-six per cent of the younger infants (group 1) consumed cheese and cheese dishes and this increased to 76% amongst the older infants. Consumption of breakfast cereals, yogurt and biscuits increased with increasing age. Biscuits were consumed by 70% of the infants, this increased from 46% for the youngest group to almost 90% for infants from group 3. Sweets, chocolates and potato crisps were also popular, especially amongst the older infants.

Vitamins or other dietary supplements

When a full term infant is receiving sufficient quantities of either breast milk from an adequately nourished mother or infant formula, vitamin deficiencies are unlikely to develop. However with the introduction of solid food and unmodified cows milk, an adequate intake of vitamins may be less certain. It is recommended that vitamin supplements should be given to infants and young children aged from six months up to at least two years and preferably five years (DHSS, 1988). A little under half of the sample (45%) were receiving dietary supplements, principally 'children's vitamin drops' largely at the recommended dosage of five drops per day. The supplements which provide vitamins A, C and D were mainly obtained by purchasing them at the clinic; however almost a quarter of mothers of infants who were taking vitamin drops obtained them free through the Welfare Food Scheme. The use of vitamin supplements was similar in all age groups.

Amongst infants who continued to receive breast milk 47% were given additional vitamin supplements. The percentage was similar amongst consumers of whole cows milk and infant formulas where vitamin supplements were consumed by 48% and 44% respectively. Additionally, 1% of infants were given cod liver oil, usually at a dose of one teaspoon (vitamin A 600µg, vitamin D 5µg, vitamin E 3.35mg) daily or once a week. Few infants were receiving the fluoride supplementation, which is recommended in areas where the fluoride concentration of the domestic water supply is less than 0.3ppm, in order to reduce the prevalence of dental caries (DHSS, 1988). One infant was given iron whilst another was taking malt extract.

Table 7.11 Dietary supplement use by age group

Age group	1 %	2 %	3 %	Total %
Children's vitamin drops	44	46	41	43
Cod liver oil	0.5	4	0	1
Fluoride	2	2	1	1
Other (iron and malt extract)	0.5	0	1	0.6

Percentages given as whole numbers except when they are less than one.

Details of the nutrient intake and contribution that supplements made to the intake of those infants given vitamin supplements are outlined in Chapter 14.

8 The range and quantities of foods consumed

Information on the quantities of individual foods consumed during the seven day record by each infant was recorded in the diary. However, 27 mothers were unable to complete the food diary for the entire week. These records have not been excluded. Intakes of foods were averaged over the number of days a record of consumption was kept.

Foods were assigned to one of 34 main groups for analyses (see Appendix VIII). Some main groups have been subdivided in order to show more detail (see Appendix IX).

Tables 8.1 and 8.2 show, for infants aged 6–9 months and 9–12 months respectively, mean and median consumption of foods for infants who consumed the food during the recording period and for all infants. Information on typical portion sizes for groups of foods and the main foods within each are presented for infants aged 6–12 months (Table 8.3). A portion size refers to the average quantity of a specified food or food group eaten by the infant at any one time. Intakes were found to be skewed and therefore median intakes are compared.

In addition to milks (cows milk, infant formulas, breast milk, etc.) most infants aged 6–12 months consumed both commercial infant foods and 'family foods'. Infants aged 9–12 months tended to eat both a greater quantity and a wider variety of most foods compared to the younger infants (6–9 months). On average more 'family foods' were eaten by the older infants, whereas infants aged 6–9 months tended to consume larger amounts of commercial infant foods, with the exception of infant fruit juices and drinks.

Almost 80% of the total sample consumed bread and breakfast cereals during the recording period. In general white bread was consumed more often than wholemeal bread (consumed by 53% and 34% respectively of bread consumers). Weetabix type cereal, instant oat cereals e.g. 'Ready Brek' and cornflakes were the most commonly consumed breakfast cereals. Biscuits and cakes were also popular especially amongst the older infants (9–12 months).

Cows milk was consumed by 84% of the sample during the recording period. Although the majority of cows milk consumed was whole milk, seven per cent received some semi-skimmed milk and just under five per cent some skimmed milk. Fewer of the younger infants drank cows milk (74% compared to 96%). But a greater

Table 8.1 Consumption of food groups by infants 6–9 months (g/infant/week)

Food group	Consumers			All infants 6–9 months	
	Mean	Median	% who ate	Mean	Median
Pasta and rice	127	93	25	31	0
Breakfast cereals	108	100	66	72	42
Bread	93	69	65	60	23
Biscuits and crispbread	43	25	50	21	0
Cakes, buns and puddings	194	128	52	101	17
Milk	2106	1937	74	1551	711
Cream and ice-cream	36	28	12	4	0
Yogurt	276	218	37	102	0
Cheese and cheese dishes	62	28	34	21	0
Eggs and egg dishes	88	60	55	49	18
Fat spreads	19	12	57	11	3
Meat, meat products and dishes	174	110	61	106	40
Offal and offal dishes	72	30	9	6	0
Poultry and poultry dishes	81	40	32	26	0
Fish products	68	45	35	24	0
Vegetables excluding potatoes	147	102	66	98	45
Potatoes	158	108	70	111	72
Fruit	202	140	67	135	80
Nuts and nut spreads	19	19	3	0.5	0
Preserves	33	17	18	6	0
Chocolate confectionery	29	20	34	10	0
Sugar confectionery	16	16	1	0.1	0
Crisps and savoury snacks	13	7	7	1	0
Fruit juices	240	138	22	53	0
Tea and coffee	713	396	27	191	0
Squash and soft drinks	557	297	21	119	0
Water	705	616	73	516	338
Miscellaneous foods	192	110	65	124	40
Commercial infant foods					
Foods in jars and cans	1039	795	74	769	512
Instant food (dried)	194	150	70	136	77
Rusks	79	54	59	46	15
Infant formulas	3529	3391	52	1833	143
Fruit juices and drinks	716	445	67	483	200
Breast milk	2665	2425	19	517	0

Median value is zero when less than 50% of the infants consumed a food group in the recording week.
Quantity of squashes, fruit juices are as consumed, i.e. where necessary a dilution factor has been applied.

number consumed infant formulas (52% compared to 20% of the older infants) and breast milk (19% compared to 10%).

Eggs and egg dishes were consumed by 62% of the sample mainly as scrambled or boiled eggs. Egg yolk was more popular than egg white. Cheese and cheese dishes were consumed by 44% of the infants. Although the median intake was similar for both age groups there was a greater number of consumers amongst older infants (56% compared with 34%).

Thirty-seven per cent of the sample consumed poultry and poultry dishes, whereas 73% ate other meats (beef, pork and lamb) and meat products. Meat was often eaten in the form of stews and casseroles and therefore the average weights of food recorded are larger than the actual quantity of meat consumed. During the survey week 26% of infants ate sausages but few ate offal. Fish was more popular in

Table 8.2 Consumption of food groups by infants 9–12 months (g/infant/week)

Food group	Consumers			All infants 9–12 months	
	Mean	Median	% who ate	Mean	Median
Pasta and rice	144	90	53	76	17
Breakfast cereals	137	128	91	124	120
Bread	140	113	95	133	109
Biscuits and crispbread	57	46	86	49	41
Cakes, buns and puddings	233	189	76	177	143
Milk	2905	2960	96	2791	2890
Cream and ice-cream	60	42	23	13	0
Yogurt	369	312	57	210	125
Cheese and cheese dishes	67	39	56	37	7
Eggs and egg dishes	130	108	70	90	54
Fat spreads	29	24	90	26	21
Meat, meat products and dishes	203	175	87	177	146
Offal and offal dishes	72	40	14	10	0
Poultry and poultry dishes	67	40	43	29	0
Fish products	71	56	56	40	19
Vegetables excluding potatoes	214	171	90	193	155
Potatoes	238	198	90	215	180
Fruit	212	175	76	160	120
Nuts and nut spreads	19	15	6	1	0
Preserves	31	25	37	11	0
Chocolate confectionery	37	27	56	21	7
Sugar confectionery	28	18	11	3	0
Crisps and savoury snacks	30	20	33	10	0
Fruit juices	346	149	38	132	0
Tea and coffee	1210	792	45	542	0
Squash and soft drinks	870	657	47	408	0
Water	605	340	46	276	0
Miscellaneous foods	230	160	86	198	120
Commercial infant foods					
Foods in jars and cans	938	743	51	481	128
Instant food (dried)	164	100	28	46	0
Rusks	63	41	42	26	0
Infant formulas	2927	2887	20	585	0
Fruit juices and drinks	811	414	43	353	0
Breast milk	1313	1050	10	131	0

Median value is zero when less than 50% of the infants consumed a food group in the recording week.
Quantity of squashes, fruit juices are as consumed, i.e. where necessary a dilution factor has been applied.

the older infants, particularly in the form of fish fingers. Overall 45% of the sample consumed fish and fish products.

Over 70% of the sample ate potatoes, vegetables and fruit at some time during the recording week. Potatoes were commonly consumed in both age groups, mainly as boiled potatoes; chips were eaten by 27% of the sample. In general, greater quantities of vegetables particularly baked beans, carrots and peas were consumed by the older infants. Brussels sprouts were in season at the time of the survey and were also popular. The most popular fruits were bananas and apples (raw or cooked). Average weekly consumption of bananas amongst consumers (56%) was 139g (median 105g) with an average portion size of 61g (median 50g) corresponding to half a large banana. Other popular desserts were yogurts, milk puddings and ice-cream. Indeed, apart from infant foods, milks and other drinks, yogurt was the food that was consumed in the largest quantity. The popularity of yogurt as a weaning food may lie in its convenience and the acceptability of the texture and taste to infants.

Table 8.3 Total quantities (g) of food consumed during the 7 day recording period (g/infant/week)

Food group	Consumers			Typical portion size (g)	
	Mean	Median	% who ate	Mean	Median
Pasta and rice	138	90	38	67	54
Breakfast cereals	124	116	78	21	20
Bread	119	93	79	20	17
of which					
—white, fresh	58	42	44	21	21
—wholemeal, fresh	74	44	31	23	18
Biscuits and crispbread	51	40	67	13	10
of which					
—semi-sweet biscuits	24	14	32	9	7
Cakes, buns and puddings	216	160	63	64	58
of which					
—milk pudding	120	156	28	90	80
Milk	2535	2614	84	136	125
of which					
—whole	2356	2273	76	135	120
—semi-skimmed	1862	1749	7	266	250
—skimmed	821	333	5	137	142
Cream and ice-cream	51	34	17	31	28
of which					
—ice-cream	52	34	15	33	28
Yogurt	330	291	46	107	125
Cheese and cheese dishes	65	34	44	27	14
of which					
—cheddar type	32	28	30	18	14
Eggs and egg dishes	110	81	62	40	36
of which					
—scrambled egg	92	60	38	61	54
—egg, boiled white	50	36	24	33	36
—egg, boiled yolk	26	18	31	17	18
Fat spreads	25	19	73	4	3
Meat, meat products and dishes	190	143	73	54	40
of which					
—sausages	45	30	26	31	24
—meat casserole with vegetables and potatoes	156	120	19	107	100
—beef, not casseroled	30	20	17	23	20
—lamb, not casseroled	25	20	10	19	13
—pork, not casseroled	24	20	8	19	10
Offal and offal dishes	72	35	11	54	40
of which					
—liver casserole with vegetables and potatoes	158	100	2	109	100
Poultry and poultry dishes	74	40	37	45	20
of which					
—chicken/turkey, not casseroled	33	20	28	23	20
Fish products	70	56	45	42	30
of which					
—white, poached, steamed	47	45	11	37	30
—fish fingers	50	56	23	41	30
Vegetables excluding potatoes	184	144	77	28	18
of which					
—baked beans	101	72	30	61	48
—carrots, fresh, boiled	59	40	51	26	18
—peas, fresh, boiled	45	31	32	22	18
Potatoes	201	153	80	49	36
of which					
—boiled	169	117	75	52	42
—chips	52	40	27	32	28
Fruit	207	167	71	55	50
of which					
—banana	139	105	56	61	50
—apple, fresh, raw	94	60	25	57	60
—apple, stewed	94	80	18	56	51

Table 8.3 Total quantities (g) of food consumed during the 7 day recording period (g/infant/week)—*continued*

Food group	Consumers			Typical portion size (g)	
	Mean	Median	% who ate	Mean	Median
Nuts and nut spreads	19	18	4	9	6
Preserves	32	20	27	11	9
Chocolate confectionery	34	26	45	14	13
of which					
—white chocolate	23	13	28	13	12
—milk chocolate	23	17	20	13	10
Sugar confectionery	27	16	6	17	9
Crisps and other savoury snacks	27	16	19	12	11
Fruit juice	304	149	30	37	27
Tea and coffee as drunk	1011	666	35	131	113
Squash and soft drinks	764	545	33	101	88
Miscellaneous foods	213	125	75	57	40
Commercial infant foods					
Meat based meal in jar/can	541	496	48	114	128
Instant meat based meal	73	60	19	20	20
Egg, cheese or fish in jar/can	202	128	17	116	128
Instant egg, cheese or fish meal	60	49	14	23	24
Cereals in jar/can	255	187	29	110	128
Instant cereals	98	78	32	24	24
Fruit based desserts in jar/can	374	300	45	102	128
Instant fruit dessert	59	45	19	18	16
Vegetable based meal in jar/can	186	150	8	120	128
Instant vegetable based meal	77	50	18	22	20
Rusks	71	48	51	16	16
Infant formulas	3375	3320	37	154	156
Fruit juices and drinks	751	432	56	94	73
Breast milk	2239*	2025*	15	105*	108*

*Estimated value.
Many infants consumed more than one type of breakfast cereal during the recording week.
Quantity of squashes, fruit juices are as consumed, i.e., where necessary a dilution factor has been applied.

Older infants consumed more crisps, confectionery and fruit juices than younger infants; commercial infant fruit juices and drinks were more popular among infants aged 6–9 months.

Younger infants tended to consume greater quantities of all types of commercial infant foods than the older infants. Prepared food in cans and jars, particularly the meat and poultry dishes, were more popular than the instant or dried type of meals. Rusks remained popular amongst the older infants.

It is difficult to compare the patterns of infant feeding in this survey with other studies as the groupings of foods may be different. However, the sources of energy were similar to those which were reported for the earlier localised studies (Black et al., 1976; McKillop and Durnin, 1982). Infants appear now to obtain a greater proportion of energy from commercial infant foods and a smaller proportion from confectionery, cakes, biscuits and preserves than they did in the past.

9 Nutrient intakes

introduction

Each mother was asked to record all food and drink consumed by her infant over a seven day period. However, 27 mothers were unable to complete the food diary for the entire week. These records have not been excluded. Intakes of nutrients were averaged over the number of days a record of consumption was kept.

Table 9.1 Number of infants for whom a food record was kept for a specified number of days

Number of days	Number of infants
7 days	461
6 days	19
5 days	2
4 days	5
3 days	1

Most of the nutritional analyses presented in this report are based on the average daily nutrients from food sources only. Data showing the distributions of specific nutrients are included where relevant. Intakes including the contribution from vitamin supplements are incorporated at the end of sections on vitamins A, C and D and also summarised in a separate chapter at the end of the report (Chapter 14).

All foods were allocated to one of five basic food types:

1. commercial infant foods excluding infant formulas but including infant juices/drinks;

2. 'family foods' excluding cows milk;

3. cows milk;

4. infant formulas; and

5. breast milk.

These groups have been further divided into 27 'family food' groups and six infant food groups (Appendix VIII). The data have been summarised into 15 broad groups (Appendix IX) with more detail shown where relevant.

The data are presented according to:

Age

Sex

Socioeconomic groups

Only child or siblings in the household

Diet reported to consist of mainly commercial infant foods, mainly 'family foods' or both

Users and non-users of vitamin supplements

Region

Type of milk predominantly used

Procedure for calculating nutrient intakes

Intakes of 38 nutrients and energy were calculated from the records of food consumption using a specially constructed nutrient data bank (for details of nutrients measured see Appendix VII). This incorporated data from a MAFF analytical study of a wide range of grouped samples of commercial infant foods and drinks which had been purchased from retail outlets, and other MAFF unpublished data. Other sources of information were McCance and Widdowson's 'The Composition of Foods' (4th edition) (Paul and Southgate, 1978), 'Cereal and Cereal Products'. The third supplement of McCance and Widdowson's 'The Composition of Foods' (4th edition), (Holland et al., 1988), published scientific literature, manufacturers, data and, where appropriate, food composition tables from other countries. For some foods no reliable information was available for certain nutrients. These values have not been taken as zero, but a likely value has been calculated from ingredients or estimated from similar foods.

Dietary Reference Values (DRVs)

The nutrient intakes of infants were compared with the Dietary Reference Values for Food Energy and Nutrients for the United Kingdom (DRVs) (DH, 1991) which replace the Recommended Daily Amounts (RDAs) (DHSS, 1979). The Dietary Reference Values apply to groups of healthy people.

1. The Reference Nutrient Intake (RNI) for protein or a vitamin or mineral is defined as an amount of the nutrient that is enough, or more than enough, for about 97% of people in a group. If the average intake of a group is at the RNI, then the risk of deficiency in the group is very small (DH, 1991).

2. The Lower Reference Nutrient Intake (LRNI) for protein or a vitamin or mineral is an amount of the nutrient that is enough for only the few people in a group who have low needs. Intakes below this level are almost certainly inadequate for most individuals (DH, 1991).

Appendix X contains more information on DRVs and their uses in evaluating data from dietary surveys.

Comparison of average nutrient intakes with the Dietary Reference Values

The age groups (6–9 months; 9–12 months) used in this report were selected to enable comparison with the 1979 UK RDA report (DHSS, 1979) that was current at the time of the survey.

The recent report on 'Dietary References Values' (DH, 1991) uses different age groups i.e.,
7–9 months
10–12 months.

For most nutrients, the Reference Nutrient Intake (RNI) (which is broadly comparable with the old RDA) does not vary between 6 and 12 months. However there are differences for protein, thiamin, niacin equivalent, vitamin B_6, magnesium and sodium.

For this report the age groups have not been changed.

Nutrient intakes for infants aged 6–12 months and comparisons with the current RNIs

Besides zinc (90% of the RNI) and vitamin D (50% of the RNI), average intakes of nutrients from food were well above the Reference Nutrient Intakes (RNIs). Supplements provided additional vitamin D in 43% of the sample which enabled these infants to meet the RNI. Sunlight can also be a significant contributor of vitamin D. Although average intakes of zinc were greater than the estimated average requirement of 3.8mg, 6% of infants were below the Lower Reference Nutrient Intake of 3.0mg (LRNI). Median intake of iron was below the RNI (90% of the RNI).

Table 9.2 Comparison of the recorded nutrient intake for infants aged 6–12 months and the RNI

Nutrient		Mean	Median	RNI	% of weighted RNI†
Energy	(kcal)	868	842	765–920	103
Protein	(g)	30.7	30.4	13.7–14.9	215
Thiamin	(mg)	1.1	1.0	0.2–0.3	445
Riboflavin	(mg)	1.5	1.5	0.4	375
Niacin equivalent	(mg)	12.5	12.1	4–5	280
Vitamin B_6	(mg)	0.8	0.8	0.3–0.4	231
Vitamin B_{12}	(µg)	3.2	3.0	0.4	800
Folate	(µg)	106	102	50	212
Vitamin C*	(mg)	100	81	25	400
Retinol equivalent*	(µg)	765	670	350	219
Vitamin D*	(µg)	3.5	1.2	7.0	50
Calcium	(mg)	783	767	525	149
Phosphorus	(mg)	742	739	400	185
Magnesium	(mg)	124	125	75–80	160
Sodium	(mg)	756	705	320–350	226
Potassium	(mg)	1352	1340	700	193
Chloride	(mg)	1205	1125	500	241
Iron*	(mg)	8.1	7	7.8	104
Zinc	(mg)	4.5	4.4	5.0	90
Copper	(mg)	0.6	0.5	0.3	200
Iodine	(µg)	204	196	60	340

*Skewed distribution.
†In order to present the average nutrient intakes for all the study infants as a percentage of the RNI (EAR for energy), the RNI was weighted according to age (and sex for the energy calculation) as appropriate.

Average, median and upper and lower 2.5 percentile of intakes for all nutrients measured and not just those which have RNIs are presented in Tables 9.3–9.7.

Table 9.3 Average daily nutrient intake for infants aged 6–12 months (n=448)

Nutrient		Mean	Median	SD	Lower 2.5%	Upper 2.5%
Energy	kcal	868	842	210	543	1402
	MJ	3.65	3.54	0.88	2.28	5.91
Protein	g	30.7	30.4	9.4	15.0	52.8
Fat	g	35.6	34.1	10.6	19.6	61.6
Starch	g	41.7	40.5	15.9	14.9	79.3
Total sugars	g	71.7	69.2	19.8	42.5	116.3
Dietary fibre	g	4.2	3.9	1.9	1.3	9.2
Sodium	mg	756	705	355	238	1478
Potassium	mg	1352	1340	376	681	2190
Calcium	mg	783	767	260	334	1433
Magnesium	mg	124	125	39	54	212
Phosphorus	mg	742	739	241	302	1294
Iron	mg	8.1	7.0	4.1	2.7	18.1
Copper	mg	0.6	0.5	0.2	0.3	1.1
Zinc	mg	4.5	4.4	1.2	2.7	7.4
Chloride	mg	1205	1125	533	438	2330
Iodine	µg	204	196	85	69	395
Manganese	mg	1.2	1.1	0.5	0.4	2.4
Retinol	µg	581	449	444	157	1707
Carotene	µg	1104	829	834	225	3140
Retinol equivalent	µg	765	670	463	282	1873
Vitamin D	µg	3.5	1.2	4.3	0.2	14.5
Vitamin E	mg	4.0	3.2	2.3	1.4	9.9
Thiamin	mg	1.1	1.0	0.4	0.5	2.0
Riboflavin	mg	1.5	1.5	0.6	0.6	2.8
Niacin	mg	5.5	4.7	2.8	1.9	12
Niacin equivalent	mg	12.5	12.1	3.5	7.2	20.9
Vitamin C	mg	100	81	80	15	318
Vitamin B_6	mg	0.8	0.8	0.3	0.3	1.4
Vitamin B_{12}	µg	3.2	3.0	1.2	1.0	6.1
Folate	µg	106	102	28	58	172
Pantothenic acid	mg	3.7	3.4	1.3	1.9	7.0
Biotin	µg	25.0	22.0	21.9	10.9	70.6
Saturated fatty acids	g	17.6	16.9	5.9	8.7	31.5
Monounsaturated fatty acids	g	10.8	10.4	3.4	5.5	18.9
Polyunsaturated fatty acids	g	3.5	3.1	1.5	1.5	7.4
Cholesterol	mg	165	155	70	55	332
Glucose	g	7.4	6.1	4.9	1.5	21.5
Fructose	g	6.5	5.4	4.6	1.0	19.2
Sucrose	g	18.5	16.6	9.7	4.3	43.3
Maltose	g	1.5	0.8	2.1	0.1	7.4
Lactose	g	35.3	32.1	16.8	8.6	77.3
Others/Dextrins	g	2.5	1.3	3.3	0.0	12.4

Niacin equivalent is the total amount of niacin consumed plus one sixtieth of the weight (in mg) of tryptophan.

Nutrient intakes by age

Older infants (9–12 months) consumed more food and a greater variety of foods and tended on average to have markedly higher intakes of macronutrients. However infants aged 6–9 months had significantly greater average daily intakes of iron (p<0.01), retinol (p<0.01), vitamin C (p<0.01), vitamin D (p<0.01), vitamin E (p<0.01), thiamin (p<0.01), niacin (p<0.01), pantothenic acid (p<0.01), lactose (p<0.01) and 'other sugars' largely galactose and dextrins (p<0.01) compared with those aged 9–12 months. These differences were largely due to the reduced consumption of infant formulas by older infants. In addition the decline in the relative importance of commercial infant foods, many of which are fortified, contributed to the older infants having mean intakes of iron, vitamin D and vitamin C which corresponded to 72%, 45% and 69% of the average intakes observed for the younger infants.

Table 9.4 Average daily nutrient intake for males aged 6–9 months (n=130)

Nutrient		Mean	Median	SD	Lower 2.5%	Upper 2.5%
Energy	kcal	836	837	163	527	1177
	MJ	3.52	3.52	0.68	2.22	4.95
Protein	g	28.1	27.5	8.1	15.0	46.2
Fat	g	33.5	33.1	8.0	19.5	51.8
Starch	g	38.9	38.1	16.6	13.5	83.1
Total sugars	g	73.4	71.5	18.6	42.6	116.2
Dietary fibre	g	3.8	3.6	1.8	1.3	8.7
Sodium	mg	606	558	286	220	1258
Potassium	mg	1286	1283	323	656	1948
Calcium	mg	760	752	236	347	1318
Magnesium	mg	114	113	35	51	180
Phosphorus	mg	683	683	217	281	1108
Iron	mg	9.6	9.2	4.1	3.3	19.3
Copper	mg	0.6	0.5	0.2	0.2	1.1
Zinc	mg	4.5	4.5	1.0	2.7	6.3
Chloride	mg	991	884	436	420	1973
Iodine	μg	178	163	74	69	342
Manganese	mg	1.1	1.1	0.5	0.3	2.5
Retinol	μg	621	519	388	172	1507
Carotene	μg	1173	875	891	258	3185
Retinol equivalent	μg	816	733	404	298	1757
Vitamin D	μg	4.9	2.1	5.0	0.1	17.1
Vitamin E	mg	4.6	3.9	2.4	1.5	10.2
Thiamin	mg	1.2	1.1	0.4	0.5	2.0
Riboflavin	mg	1.6	1.6	0.6	0.5	3.0
Niacin	mg	6.5	6.1	2.9	1.7	12.6
Niacin equivalent	mg	12.9	12.8	3.2	6.5	20.7
Vitamin C	mg	114	105	73	18	300
Vitamin B_6	mg	0.9	0.9	0.3	0.3	1.3
Vitamin B_{12}	μg	3.0	3.1	1.1	0.8	5.9
Folate	μg	109	107	27	60	168
Pantothenic acid	mg	4.0	4.0	1.3	1.9	7.0
Biotin	μg	26.6	23.2	22.7	10.5	118.7
Saturated fatty acids	g	16.1	16	4.5	8.3	26.1
Monounsaturated fatty acids	g	10.0	10.2	2.7	5.4	16.1
Polyunsaturated fatty acids	g	3.3	2.9	1.5	1.2	7.8
Cholesterol	mg	151	145	62	47	292
Glucose	g	7.0	6.0	4.3	1.5	17.5
Fructose	g	6.5	5.4	4.5	1.0	18.9
Sucrose	g	15.9	13.9	8.5	4.1	34.8
Maltose	g	1.5	0.9	2.0	0.1	8.6
Lactose	g	39.2	36.3	18.0	6.0	90.7
Others/Dextrins	g	3.3	1.7	3.8	0.0	14.1

Niacin equivalent is the total amount of niacin consumed plus one sixtieth of the weight (in mg) of tryptophan.

Nutrient intakes by sex

Infants aged 6–9 months (Tables 9.4 and 9.5)

Males had greater intakes of nutrients with the exception of retinol and maltose. Differences were significant for intakes of energy (p<0.05), dietary fibre (p<0.025), potassium (p<0.025), zinc (p<0.05), manganese (p<0.01), carotene (p<0.01), vitamin B_6 (p<0.01) and folate (p<0.01).

Table 9.5 Average daily nutrient intake for females aged 6–9 months (n=128)

Nutrient		Mean	Median	SD	Lower 2.5%	Upper 2.5%
Energy	kcal	795	751	207	476	1204
	MJ	3.34	3.17	0.87	2.00	5.06
Protein	g	26.7	25.1	8.3	13.9	47.7
Fat	g	32.3	30.8	9.4	18.6	50.9
Starch	g	35.9	34.5	13.5	10.1	69.4
Total sugars	g	70.1	66.1	22.4	37.3	129.7
Dietary fibre	g	3.4	3.2	1.5	1.0	7.4
Sodium	mg	571	538	265	216	1243
Potassium	mg	1190	1151	341	565	2086
Calcium	mg	729	676	254	299	1503
Magnesium	mg	107	102	36	43	190
Phosphorus	mg	653	641	228	229	1240
Iron	mg	9.0	8.2	4.4	2.8	20.6
Copper	mg	0.6	0.5	0.2	0.3	1.1
Zinc	mg	4.2	4.0	1.1	2.7	7.0
Chloride	mg	927	857	394	383	1786
Iodine	µg	175	164	74	56	335
Manganese	mg	1.0	1.0	0.4	0.4	1.9
Retinol	µg	602	509	380	166	1708
Carotene	µg	880	692	639	191	2214
Retinol equivalent	µg	748	678	389	295	1871
Vitamin D	µg	4.5	2.4	4.6	0.2	14.2
Vitamin E	mg	4.4	3.7	2.5	1.4	10.0
Thiamin	mg	1.1	1.1	0.4	0.4	2.2
Riboflavin	mg	1.5	1.4	0.6	0.5	2.8
Niacin	mg	5.9	5.2	3.0	2.0	11.7
Niacin equivalent	mg	12.0	11.4	3.7	7.2	21.7
Vitamin C	mg	119	92	90	19	385
Vitamin B_6	mg	0.8	0.8	0.3	0.3	1.3
Vitamin B_{12}	µg	3.0	2.9	1.2	0.5	6.2
Folate	µg	100	95	26	53	155
Pantothenic acid	mg	3.8	3.5	1.4	2.0	7.0
Biotin	µg	26.4	21.1	27.4	12.1	152.4
Saturated fatty acids	g	15.7	15.1	5.1	8.2	27.3
Monounsaturated fatty acids	g	9.6	9.3	2.9	4.9	16.7
Polyunsaturated fatty acids	g	3.1	2.7	1.5	1.4	6.7
Cholesterol	mg	147	140	52	58	272
Glucose	g	7.1	5.7	5.3	1.1	22.9
Fructose	g	6.1	4.9	4.9	0.4	20.4
Sucrose	g	14.6	13.4	7.8	2.5	37.8
Maltose	g	1.7	1.0	2.6	0.1	11.8
Lactose	g	37.3	35.9	17.0	4.9	77.0
Others/Dextrins	g	3.3	1.6	3.9	0.0	14.6

Niacin equivalent is the total amount of niacin consumed plus one sixtieth of the weight (in mg) of tryptophan.

Infants aged 9–12 months (Tables 9.6 and 9.7)

In common with the younger infants, males had greater intakes of all nutrients except for retinol and maltose. Intakes of energy (p<0.05), starch (p<0.01), total sugars (p<0.05), dietary fibre (p<0.05), magnesium (p<0.05), copper (p<0.05), manganese (p<0.05), riboflavin (p<0.05), niacin (p<0.05), folate (p<0.05), and sucrose (p<0.025) were significantly greater than in females.

Table 9.6   Average daily nutrient intake for males aged 9–12 months (n=96)

Nutrient		Mean	Median	SD	Lower 2.5%	Upper 2.5%
Energy	kcal	960	950	201	609	1480
	MJ	4.04	4.00	0.84	2.56	6.21
Protein	g	35.1	34.9	8.4	20.7	57.2
Fat	g	39.4	39.6	11.4	20.1	69.1
Starch	g	49.5	47.0	15.3	24.5	97.2
Total sugars	g	74.5	73.2	19.7	39.7	126.4
Dietary fibre	g	5.0	4.6	1.8	2.4	9.8
Sodium	mg	963	937	321	436	1592
Potassium	mg	1526	1501	334	871	2320
Calcium	mg	849	814	269	346	1494
Magnesium	mg	145	141	32	83	218
Phosphorus	mg	843	840	218	415	1404
Iron	mg	7.2	6.0	3.7	2.6	17.0
Copper	mg	0.6	0.6	0.2	0.3	1.2
Zinc	mg	4.9	4.9	1.1	2.3	7.7
Chloride	mg	1510	1478	479	756	2514
Iodine	μg	237	242	79	88	418
Manganese	mg	1.3	1.2	0.5	0.6	2.5
Retinol	μg	505	391	351	110	1681
Carotene	μg	1238	968	1004	184	4837
Retinol equivalent	μg	711	593	396	209	1840
Vitamin D	μg	2.3	0.9	3.9	0.1	16.6
Vitamin E	mg	3.7	3.1	2.2	1.3	11.0
Thiamin	mg	1.1	0.9	0.4	0.6	2.1
Riboflavin	mg	1.6	1.5	0.5	0.7	3.4
Niacin	mg	5.0	4.1	2.6	2.2	12.6
Niacin equivalent	mg	12.9	12.4	3.3	7.7	22.1
Vitamin C	mg	87	63	80	15	336
Vitamin B_6	mg	0.9	0.8	0.2	0.5	1.5
Vitamin B_{12}	μg	3.4	3.2	1.1	1.6	6.1
Folate	μg	111	108	30	56	187
Pantothenic acid	mg	3.6	3.3	1.2	1.9	7.1
Biotin	μg	24.3	21.6	19.7	9.5	45.3
Saturated fatty acids	g	19.9	20.5	6.2	8.2	33.3
Monounsaturated fatty acids	g	12.2	12.0	3.6	6.3	21.7
Polyunsaturated fatty acids	g	3.9	3.5	1.5	1.9	8.7
Cholesterol	mg	184	172	75	48	362
Glucose	g	7.8	6.6	4.9	1.4	21.4
Fructose	g	7.2	6.3	4.8	1.2	20.2
Sucrose	g	24.0	21.8	11.6	5.1	52.7
Maltose	g	1.2	0.7	1.9	0.1	5.5
Lactose	g	32.9	29.5	17.8	9.8	96.8
Others/Dextrins	g	1.5	1.0	2.1	0.0	10.7

Niacin equivalent is the total amount of niacin consumed plus one sixtieth of the weight (in mg) of tryptophan.

Table 9.7 Average daily nutrient intake for females aged 9–12 months (n=134)

Nutrient		Mean	Median	SD	Lower 2.5%	Upper 2.5%
Energy	kcal	905	841	229	568	1516
	MJ	3.81	3.54	0.96	2.39	6.36
Protein	g	34.0	33.3	9.7	18.1	61.7
Fat	g	38.0	36.9	11.9	19.5	72.3
Starch	g	44.4	42.0	14.8	20.7	82.8
Total sugars	g	69.5	66.9	18.0	40.1	112.9
Dietary fibre	g	4.6	4.5	1.9	1.8	10.4
Sodium	mg	928	865	356	408	1915
Potassium	mg	1446	1404	407	765	2663
Calcium	mg	808	799	271	313	1589
Magnesium	mg	136	134	41	63	244
Phosphorus	mg	811	805	248	353	1479
Iron	mg	6.4	5.7	3.3	2.3	15.1
Copper	mg	0.6	0.5	0.2	0.3	1.3
Zinc	mg	4.7	4.5	1.3	2.4	7.9
Chloride	mg	1457	1371	543	661	2916
Iodine	µg	234	232	89	86	515
Manganese	mg	1.2	1.1	0.5	0.4	2.6
Retinol	µg	576	387	586	146	2533
Carotene	µg	1157	908	772	156	3058
Retinol equivalent	µg	769	617	605	284	2653
Vitamin D	µg	2.0	1.0	2.8	0.2	11.1
Vitamin E	mg	3.4	2.8	1.8	1.1	8.5
Thiamin	mg	1.0	0.9	0.4	0.4	2.1
Riboflavin	mg	1.5	1.4	0.5	0.6	2.8
Niacin	mg	4.5	4.0	2.2	1.7	11.2
Niacin equivalent	mg	12.2	11.7	3.5	7.1	21.4
Vitamin C	mg	77	56	68	15	312
Vitamin B_6	mg	0.8	0.8	0.3	0.4	1.5
Vitamin B_{12}	µg	3.4	3.1	1.4	1.2	7.3
Folate	µg	104	100	28	55	177
Pantothenic acid	mg	3.4	3.2	1.2	1.8	7.0
Biotin	µg	23.5	21.0	16.0	11.1	45.5
Saturated fatty acids	g	19.2	18.9	6.7	9.0	39.3
Monounsaturated fatty acids	g	11.8	11.3	3.6	6.1	21.1
Polyunsaturated fatty acids	g	3.7	3.5	1.5	1.6	7.3
Cholesterol	mg	183	168	81	66	357
Glucose	g	7.7	6.4	5.1	1.7	21.7
Fructose	g	6.5	5.3	4.4	1.2	17.9
Sucrose	g	20.8	19.8	8.3	7.7	42.8
Maltose	g	1.5	0.8	1.9	0.2	7.3
Lactose	g	31.2	29.0	13.4	8.9	68.7
Others/Dextrins	g	1.7	1.0	2.3	0.0	9.1

Niacin equivalent is the total amount of niacin consumed plus one sixtieth of the weight (in mg) of tryptophan.

Energy

Energy intake is expressed either in kilocalories (kcal) or megajoules (MJ) (Table 9.8).

The average daily energy intake for all the infants participating in the study was 868kcal (3.65MJ), median 842kcal (3.54MJ). There was considerable variation but the overall distribution was Gaussian.

On average, infants from the C2DE socioeconomic group tended to have higher energy intakes compared to those from the ABC1 socioeconomic group. However, this difference was only significant ($p < 0.01$) among the older infants from C2DE socioeconomic group [949kcal (3.99MJ), median 915kcal (3.85MJ) compared to 881kcal (3.71MJ) for those from ABC1 socioeconomic group, median 867kcal (3.66MJ)]. This trend was apparent in the earlier national survey of pre-school children carried out during 1967–68 (DHSS, 1975) and in Newcastle upon Tyne 1968–71 (Black et al., 1976). Even on a household scale, data from the National Food Survey, which records household food purchases and the nutrient value of foods consumed within the home, also support this trend.

Infants from SE, E Anglia and London had on average, daily energy intakes of 836kcal (3.52MJ), median 837kcal (3.52MJ), which is significantly lower than for those from Wales, Midlands and SW ($p < 0.01$), and from Scotland and Northern England ($p < 0.05$). Adults too from Central and SW England had slightly higher energy intakes than those from other regions (Gregory et al., 1990).

As would be expected, younger infants (6–9 months) had a significantly lower ($p < 0.01$) average daily energy intake (815kcal, median 792kcal) compared to the older infants (928kcal, median 894kcal). Distributions of energy intake for both age groups are presented in Figures 9.1 and 9.2. In both age groups, males had significantly greater energy intakes than females ($p < 0.05$). Similar findings have been reported in a longitudinal study of infants aged from 2–18 months (Black et al., 1983).

In this survey average energy intake met the estimated average requirement.

Contribution of main food types to total energy intakes

There was little difference in the contribution of main food types to energy intake between sexes. Differences were marked between age groups with the older infants (aged 9–12 months) obtaining a greater proportion of their energy from 'family foods' (see Figure 9.3 and Tables 9.9 and 9.10 for greater detail).

Amongst the older infants (9–12 months) those from C2DE socio-economic group derived a greater proportion of energy from infant formulas (8%) compared with those from ABC1 socioeconomic group (3%). The variation in feeding patterns with socioeconomic group is described in more detail in Chapter 11.

Table 9.8a Average daily energy intake (kcal) by different variables (age, sex, socioeconomic group, presence of siblings or not)

Variable	Number	Mean	Median	SD	Lower 2.5%	Upper 2.5%
Infants aged 6–12 months						
All	488	868	842	210	543	1402
Males	226	888	883	190	544	1313
Females	262	851	813	225	534	1488
ABC1	163	837	840	163	542	1200
C2DE	325	884	884	229	543	1501
Scotland + N England	178	872	839	209	497	1457
Wales, Midlands + SW	149	899	858	241	570	1553
SE, E Anglia + London	161	836	837	175	540	1288
Infants aged 6–9 months						
All	258	815	792	187	515	1182
Males	130	836	837	163	527	1177
Females	128	795	751	207	476	1204
ABC1	91	802	781	173	455	1196
C2DE	167	822	795	194	523	1160
Only child	89	835	823	162	530	1182
Siblings	169	805	777	199	486	1191
Infants aged 9–12 months						
All	230	928	894	219	589	1510
Males	96	960	950	201	609	1480
Females	134	905	841	229	568	1516
ABC1	72	881	867	138	580	1265
C2DE	158	949	915	245	589	1523
Only child	75	903	880	204	559	1479
Siblings	155	940	905	225	582	1526

Table 9.8b Average daily energy intake (MJ) by different variables (age, sex, socioeconomic group, presence of siblings or not)

Variable	Number	Mean	Median	SD	Lower 2.5%	Upper 2.5%
Infants aged 6–12 months						
All	488	3.65	3.54	0.88	2.28	5.91
Males	226	3.74	3.72	0.8	2.29	5.53
Females	262	3.58	3.42	0.95	2.25	6.25
ABC1	163	3.5	3.51	0.68	2.27	5.02
C2DE	325	3.69	3.53	0.96	2.27	6.28
Scotland +N England	178	3.67	3.53	0.88	2.09	6.12
Wales, Midlands + SW	149	3.78	3.62	1.01	2.40	6.52
SE, E Anglia + London	161	3.52	3.52	0.73	2.28	5.41
Infants aged 6–9 months						
All	258	3.43	3.33	0.79	2.17	4.97
Males	130	3.5	3.5	0.68	2.21	4.92
Females	128	3.32	3.14	0.87	1.95	5.04
ABC1	91	3.37	3.29	0.73	1.91	5.03
C2DE	167	3.46	3.34	0.82	2.20	4.89
Only child	89	3.51	3.47	0.68	2.23	4.97
Siblings	169	3.39	3.28	0.84	2.05	5.01
Infants aged 9–12 months						
All	230	3.9	3.76	0.92	2.48	6.34
Males	96	4.02	3.98	0.84	2.55	6.19
Females	134	3.79	3.52	0.96	2.38	6.34
ABC1	72	3.71	3.66	0.58	2.44	5.32
C2DE	158	3.99	3.85	1.03	2.48	6.39
Only child	75	3.8	3.7	0.86	2.35	6.21
Siblings	155	3.95	3.81	0.95	2.45	6.41

Figure 9.1   Distribution of daily energy intake for infants aged 6–9 months

```
Count  Midpoint (kcal)
  0       25
  0       75
  0      125
  0      175
  0      225
  0      275
  0      325      .
  0      375       .
  2      425      ** .
  3      475      *** .
  6      525      ***** .
  9      575      ******** .
 22      625      ******************* .****
 22      675      ******************.*
 41      725      **************************************.***********
 29      775      **************************.**
 27      825      ************************. .
 26      875      ***********************.
 21      925      ******************* .
 13      975      ************* .
 12     1025      ************ .
 11     1075      ***********.*
  3     1125      *** .
  6     1175      ***.**
  2     1225      *.
  1     1275      .
  0     1325      .
  0     1375
  1     1425      *
  0     1475
  0     1525
                  |····+····|····+····|····+····|····+····|····+····|
                  0         4         8        12        16        20
```

Mean	815	Median	792	STD DEV		187
Minimum	433	Maximum	2186			

Percentile	Value	Percentile	Value	Percentile	Value
2.5	515	10.0	615	25.0	701
50.0	792	75.0	912	90.0	1036
97.5	1182				

Valid cases	258	Missing Cases	0

One asterisk equals approximately 1.03 occurrences.

Figure 9.2 Distribution of daily energy intake for infants aged 9–12 months

```
Count  Midpoint (kcal)
  0      25
  0      75
  0     125
  0     175
  0     225
  1     275    *
  0     325    .
  0     375    .
  1     425    *.
  0     475     .
  0     525      .
  5     575    *****:
  9     625    *********:*
  8     675    ********* .
 13     725    ************** .
 19     775    *******************:***
 37     825    *******************************************
 24     875    ************************:****
 21     925    *********************:
 28     975    *********************:********
 19    1025    ********************:
 10    1075    **********    .
  9    1125    *********   .
  3    1175    ***        .
  1    1225    *        .
  5    1275    ******.
  5    1325    *****:**
  2    1375    **.
  2    1425    *:
  1    1475    :
  4    1525    :***
               |····+····|····+····|····+····|····+····|····+····|
               0         4         8         12        16        20
```

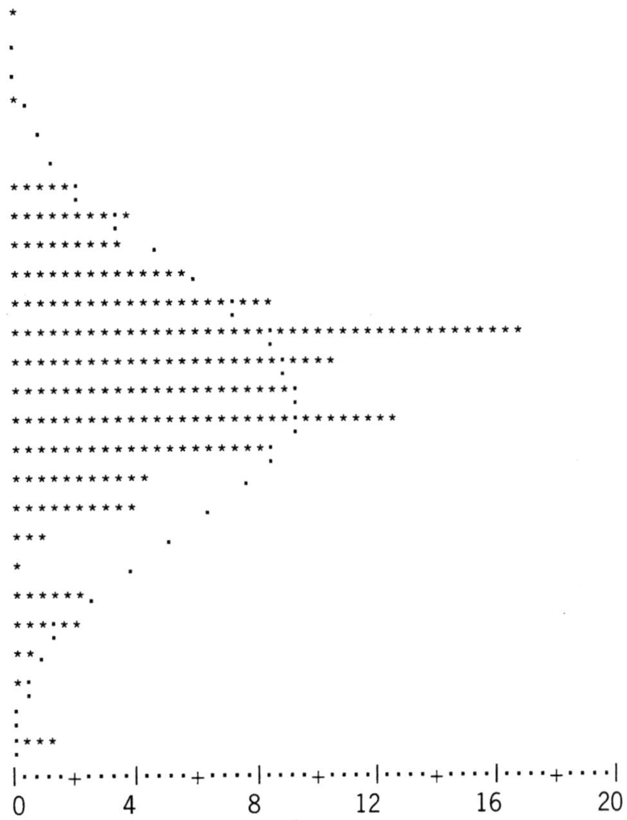

Mean	928	Median	894	STD DEV	219
Minimum	279	Maximum	1792		

Percentile	Value	Percentile	Value	Percentile	Value
2.50	589	10.00	690	25.00	801
50.00	894	75.00	1015	90.00	1214
97.50	1510				

| Valid cases | 230 | Missing Cases | 0 | | |

One asterisk equals approximately 1.03 occurrences.

Table 9.9 Average daily energy from main foods by sex (kcal/day) for infants aged 6–9 months

	Males		Females		Total	
	amount	%	amount	%	amount	%
Cereal products of which	106	13	90	11	98	12
— breakfast cereals	43	5	38	5	41	5
— bread	22	3	19	2	20	3
— biscuits, cakes, puddings	36	4	30	4	33	4
— pasta and rice	5	1	3	0	4	0
Milk and milk products of which	160	19	172	22	166	20
— cows milk	137	16	154	19	146	18
— cheese and cheese dishes	8	1	5	1	6	1
— yogurt	14	2	12	1	13	2
Eggs and egg dishes	16	2	13	2	14	2
Fat spreads	10	1	11	1	11	1
Meat and meat products	28	3	22	3	25	3
Fish and fish products	4	0	5	1	5	1
Vegetables of which	21	3	17	2	19	2
— potatoes	14	2	11	1	12	2
Fruits and nuts	19	2	14	2	17	2
Confectionery and preserves	10	1	9	1	10	1
Beverages of which	16	2	11	1	14	2
— fruit juice	4	0	2	0	3	0
— soft drinks and squashes	3	0	5	1	4	1
Miscellaneous foods	10	1	7	1	8	1
Commercial infant food of which	188	23	195	24	191	23
— foods in jars/cans	62	7	72	9	67	8
— instant/dried foods	80	10	74	9	77	9
— rusks	28	3	26	3	27	3
— fruit juices and drinks	18	2	23	3	21	3
Infant formulas	197	24	179	22	188	23
Breast milk	49	6	51	6	50	6
Total	**836**	**100**	**795**	**100**	**815**	**100**
Number of cases	130		128		258	

Table 9.10 Average daily energy from main foods by sex (kcal/day) for infants aged 9–12 months

	Males		Females		Total	
	amount	%	amount	%	amount	%
Cereal products	203	21	195	22	198	21
of which						
— breakfast cereals	73	8	67	7	70	8
— bread	45	5	46	5	46	5
— biscuits, cakes, puddings	75	8	72	8	73	8
— pasta and rice	8	1	10	1	9	1
Milk and milk products	308	32	302	33	305	33
of which						
— cows milk	263	27	258	29	261	28
— cheese and cheese dishes	15	2	14	2	14	2
— yogurt	26	3	26	3	26	3
Eggs and egg dishes	24	3	28	3	26	3
Fat spreads	24	3	27	3	26	3
Meat and meat products	47	5	46	5	47	5
Fish and fish products	8	1	11	1	10	1
Vegetables	53	5	44	5	48	5
of which						
— potatoes	29	3	26	3	27	3
Fruits and nuts	20	2	18	2	19	2
Confectionery and preserves	22	2	19	2	21	2
Beverages	53	6	37	4	43	5
of which						
— fruit juice	7	1	7	1	7	1
— squashes and soft drinks	20	2	12	1	16	2
Miscellaneous foods	13	1	14	2	14	2
Commercial infant food	107	11	92	10	98	11
of which						
— foods in jars/cans	45	5	41	4	43	5
— instant/dried foods	34	4	20	2	26	3
— rusks	15	2	15	2	15	2
— fruit juices and drinks	13	1	16	2	14	2
Infant formulas	72	8	55	6	62	7
Breast milk	7	1	17	2	13	1
Total	**960**	**100**	**905**	**100**	**928**	**100**
Number of cases	96		134		230	

Figure 9.3　Percentage contribution of food types to energy intake

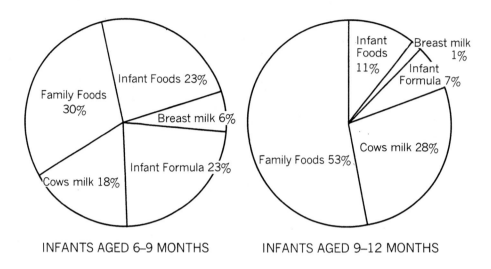

INFANTS AGED 6–9 MONTHS　　　INFANTS AGED 9–12 MONTHS

Contribution of protein, fat and carbohydrate to total energy intakes in infants aged 6–12 months

Infants who were exclusively breastfed in the first few weeks of life had on average higher energy intakes (900kcal, SD 247) compared to those who were initially bottlefed (856kcal, SD 213) or breast and bottlefed (850kcal, SD 179). However this difference was only significant (p<0.025) for infants exclusively bottlefed.

The unweaned infant relies exclusively on breast milk and or infant formula and therefore has a high fat intake (approximately 50% of energy from fat). As the process of weaning starts, with a gradual replacement of breast or formula milk with cows milk and a range of foods of suitable textures, through to the normal mixed diet of the general population, the contribution that fat makes to energy intake will change. The extent of the change depends on the selection of other foods.

The percentage contribution made by carbohydrate, protein and fat to the total energy of the diets of British infants aged 6–12 months are presented in Table 9.11 by age, sex, region and socioeconomic group. Carbohydrate, protein and fat provided a similar percentage of the energy intake for all groups although older male infants from the ABC1 socioeconomic group obtained a significantly greater (p<0.025) proportion from protein than those of similar age from the C2DE socioeconomic group. Also infants from the SE, E Anglia and London obtained significantly more (p<0.025) energy from protein compared to those from Wales, Midlands and the SW. In the older infants (aged 9–12 months) protein tended to make a slightly greater contribution and carbohydrate a slightly lower contribution to energy intake.

In this survey fat provided on average 37% of total energy intake. This was similar to the level found in the youngest children aged

Table 9.11 Proportion of energy from carbohydrate, protein, fat, saturated and polyunsaturated fatty acids

	Carbohydrate	Protein	Fat	Saturated fatty acids	Polyunsaturated fatty acids
	%	%	%	%	%
Infants aged 6–9 months					
All	50.2	13.5	36.3	17.5	3.6
Males	50.4	13.5	36.1	17.4	3.6
Females	50.0	13.5	36.5	17.7	3.5
ABC1	50.6	13.3	36.1	17.2	3.6
C2DE	50.0	13.6	36.4	17.7	3.5
Scotland + N England	50.2	13.5	36.3	17.5	3.5
Wales, Midlands + SW	50.0	13.1	36.9	17.8	3.4
SE, E Anglia + London	50.4	13.7	35.9	17.2	3.7
Infants aged 9–12 months					
All	48.0	14.9	37.1	18.8	3.7
Males	48.7	14.7	36.6	18.5	3.6
Females	47.5	15.1	37.5	18.9	3.7
ABC1	47.7	15.4	36.9	18.6	3.8
C2DE	48.1	14.7	37.2	18.8	3.6
Scotland + N England	47.5	14.9	37.6	19.2	3.5
Wales, Midlands + SW	48.5	14.7	36.8	18.5	3.7
SE, E Anglia + London	47.9	15.1	37.0	18.6	3.8

6–18 months in the earlier Department of Health survey of pre-school children (DHSS, 1975) and to that found in eight month old children in Newcastle (Black et al., 1976). However, it is lower than that found in infants aged 0.6–1 year in Glasgow where 40% of energy was provided by fat (McKillop and Durnin, 1982). Fat provided a lower proportion of energy in the diets of older infants than has been reported for adults (Gregory et al., 1990) and school children (DH, 1989a).

Fat made a larger contribution to energy intake of infants aged 6–12 months who were reported to be fed on 'family foods'. This was largely because most commercial infant foods are relatively low in fat.

In this survey the percentage of energy provided by saturated fatty acids was 18%, greater than has been reported for adults (Gregory et al., 1990) largely because infants aged 6–12 months still have a heavy reliance on milk as a major source of energy and nutrients.

Protein

Average intakes of protein were similar for males and females, but were significantly lower (p<0.01) for infants aged 6–9 months (27.4g; median 26.2g) than for those aged 9–12 months (34.4g; median 33.8g). Protein provided 13% and 15% of total energy for the younger and older infants respectively. The proportion of energy derived from protein did not vary by sex, socioeconomic group or region. Average intakes recorded in this survey were well in excess (215%) of the RNI for infants of this age.

The sources of protein differed in the two age groups (see Table 9.12). Milks including cows milk, infant formulas and breast milk were the major sources of protein providing, on average, 47% of the total intake of infants aged 6–9 months and 43% in the diets of infants aged 9–12 months. In the younger infants one fifth of the protein was provided by commercial infant food (excluding infant formulas), whereas a variety of 'family foods' such as meat, meat products and cereals, were important sources for the older infants.

Intakes and main sources of protein were similar for both socio-economic groups. However, the younger infants from the ABC1 socioeconomic group obtained twice as much protein from breast milk than infants aged 6–9 months from the C2DE socioeconomic group who derived more from infant formulas.

Table 9.12   Contribution of main food types to average daily protein (g) intake by age

	Infants 6–9 months		Infants 9–12 months		Total sample	
	amount	%	amount	%	amount	%
Cereal products of which	2.8	10	5.5	16	4.1	13
—bread	0.8	3	1.7	5	1.2	4
—breakfast cereals	1.2	4	2.0	6	1.5	5
Milk and milk products of which	8.2	30	15.0	44	11.4	37
—cows milk	7.2	26	12.9	37	9.9	32
—cheese and cheese dishes	0.4	1	0.8	2	0.6	2
—yogurt	0.6	2	1.3	4	0.9	3
Egg and egg dishes	0.8	3	1.5	4	1.1	4
Fat spreads	0.0	0	0.0	0	0.0	0
Meat and meat products	2.2	8	3.7	11	2.9	9
Fish and fish products	0.5	2	0.8	2	0.6	2
Vegetables	0.7	3	1.6	5	1.1	4
Fruits and nuts	0.2	1	0.3	1	0.2	1
Confectionery and preserves	0.1	0	0.3	1	0.2	0
Beverages	0.3	1	0.8	2	0.6	2
Miscellaneous foods	0.3	1	0.4	1	0.3	1
Commercial infant foods of which	5.5	20	2.8	8	4.2	14
—foods in jars/cans	2.5	9	1.7	5	2.1	7
—instant/dried foods	2.6	9	0.9	3	1.8	6
—rusks	0.5	2	0.3	1	0.4	1
Infant formulas	4.9	18	1.6	5	3.3	11
Breast milk	1.0	3	0.2	1	0.6	2
Total	**27.4**	**100**	**34.4**	**100**	**30.7**	**100**
Number of cases	258		230		488	

Carbohydrate

The average daily intake of total carbohydrate was significantly greater (p<0.01) for infants aged 9–12 months than the younger infants (118.1g, median 114.8g; 109.2g, median 105.5g respectively). Males had a significantly greater (p<0.01) intake of carbohydrate than females. This difference was more marked for the older infants. The percentage of energy derived from carbohydrate was similar for the two age groups providing on average 49%. This is slightly higher than the 46% that was reported for infants aged 0.6–1 year from Glasgow (McKillop and Durnin, 1982).

The types of foods which provided carbohydrate differed between the two age groups. The main sources for infants aged 6–9 months were commercial infant foods, infant formulas and breast milk (58% in total) whereas 'family foods' provided 77% of the carbohydrate intake for the older infants (9–12 months). Table 9.13 shows the contribution made by foods to carbohydrate intake.

Intakes of carbohydrate tended to be greater for infants from the C2DE socioeconomic group, although this difference was only significant (p<0.01) for older infants (9–12 months). For each age group, both socioeconomic groups obtained a similar proportion of total carbohydrate from commercial infant foods and 'family foods' although breast milk was a more important source for infants from

Table 9.13   Contribution of main food types to average daily carbohydrate (g) intake by age

	Infants 6–9 months		Infants 9–12 months		Total sample	
	amount	%	amount	%	amount	%
Cereal products of which	17.7	16	35.5	30	26.1	23
—bread	4.1	4	9.3	8	6.6	6
—breakfast cereals	8.2	7	14.3	12	11.1	10
—biscuits	2.0	2	4.5	4	3.2	3
—cakes, buns and puddings	2.7	2	5.7	5	4.1	4
Milk and milk products	13.9	13	26.4	22	19.8	17
Egg and egg dishes	0.0	0	0.2	0	0.1	0
Fat spreads	0.0	0	0.0	0	0.0	0
Meat and products	1.1	1	1.9	2	1.5	1
Fish and fish products	0.3	0	0.5	0	0.4	0
Vegetables of which	3.9	4	8.7	7	6.2	5
—potatoes	2.8	3	5.6	5	4.1	4
Fruits and nuts	4.0	4	4.4	4	4.2	4
Confectionery and preserves	1.6	1	3.5	3	2.5	2
Beverages	2.5	2	8.3	7	5.3	5
Miscellaneous foods	1.0	1	1.7	1	1.3	1
Commercial infant foods of which	36.0	33	18.5	16	27.7	24
—foods in jars/cans	11.1	10	6.8	6	9.1	8
—instant/dried foods	14.1	13	4.8	4	9.7	9
—rusks	5.3	5	3.0	3	4.2	4
—infants fruit drinks, juices	5.5	5	3.8	3	4.7	4
Infant formulas	22.1	20	7.2	6	15.1	13
Breast milk	5.0	5	1.3	1	3.3	3
Total	**109.2**	**100**	**118.1**	**100**	**113.4**	**100**
Number of cases	258		230		488	100

the ABC1 socioeconomic group. Infants from the C2DE socio-economic group derived more carbohydrate from potatoes, chocolate confectionery and biscuits compared with those from the ABC1 socioeconomic group who obtained more from yoghurt, fruit and infant fruit juices and fruit drinks. There were few regional differences in carbohydrate intake. Infants from Wales, the Midlands and SW had significantly greater carbohydrate intakes (p<0.01) compared with those from SE, E Anglia and London.

Sugars

In this survey intakes of total sugars, individual sugars and non-milk extrinsic sugars (NMES) expressed as monosaccharide equivalents were calculated. The average daily intakes of total sugars were 71.8g (median 68.2g) for infants aged 6–9 months and 71.6g (median 70.2g) for those aged 9–12 months, providing 33% and 29% of total energy respectively.

Dietary sources of, and therefore the contributions made by the individual sugars varied for each of the two age groups (Tables 9.14 and 9.15). The younger infants (6–9 months) obtained most sugars (62%) from commercial infant foods whereas 'family foods' provided 75% of the intake of the older infants.

In 1989, COMA published a report on 'Dietary sugars and human disease' (DH, 1989b). The Panel found no evidence that the

Table 9.14 Contribution of main food types to average daily intake of individual sugars (g/day) for infants aged 6–9 months (n=258)

Food Groups	Glucose	Fructose	Sucrose	Maltose	Lactose	Others	Total
Family foods							
Milk and milk products	0.0	0.0	1.8	0.1	11.3	0.3	13.6
Fruit	0.8	1.1	1.8	0.0	0.0	0.0	3.7
Biscuits, cakes and puddings	0.1	0.1	1.4	0.1	0.6	0.0	2.3
Cereals and bread	0.3	0.1	1.5	0.1	0.3	0.0	2.2
Squashes and soft drinks	0.3	0.3	0.4	0.0	0	0.0	1.1
Fruit juices	0.2	0.3	0.2	0.0	0	0.0	0.7
Other beverages	0.0	0.0	0.3	0.0	0.4	0.0	0.7
Confectionery	0.0	0.0	0.7	0.0	0.1	0.0	0.9
Vegetables and potatoes	0.1	0.1	0.5	0.0	0	0.0	0.7
Miscellaneous foods	0.5	0.3	0.3	0.0	0.1	0.0	1.2
Total family foods	**2.3**	**2.3**	**9.0**	**0.4**	**12.8**	**0.3**	**27.1**
Infant foods							
Infant formulas	0.1	0.0	0.1	0.6	18.2	2.5	21.6
Fruit juices and drinks	2.7	2.2	0.3	0.3	0.0	0.0	5.5
Prepared food in jar/can	1.2	1.5	2.4	0.0	0.8	0.1	5.9
Instant/dried foods	0.6	0.3	1.9	0.2	1.3	0.3	4.7
Rusks	0.1	0.0	1.6	0.1	0.1	0.1	1.9
Breast milk	0.0	0.0	0.0	0.0	5.0	0.0	5.0
Total infant food	**4.7**	**4.0**	**6.3**	**1.2**	**25.4**	**3.0**	**44.6**
Total food	**7.0**	**6.3**	**15.3**	**1.6**	**38.3**	**3.3**	**71.8**

Milk and milk products includes milks, ice-creams, creams and yogurt but excludes cheese. Cereals and bread includes pasta, rice and breakfast cereals. Miscellaneous foods includes all meat, fish, cheese, eggs and products and dishes containing these; also fat spreads, nuts and nut spreads, preserves, honey, crisps and savoury snacks. Other beverages includes tea, coffee, cocoa, malted milk drink.

Table 9.15 Contribution of main food types to average daily intake of individual sugars (g/day) for infants aged 9–12 months (n=230)

Food Groups	Glucose	Fructose	Sucrose	Maltose	Lactose	Others	Total
Family foods							
Milk and milk products	0.1	0.1	4.0	0.1	20.6	0.7	25.7
Fruit	0.9	1.3	1.9	0.0	0.0	0.0	4.1
Biscuits, cakes and puddings	0.3	0.2	3.5	0.2	0.9	0.0	5.2
Cereals and bread	0.7	0.2	2.9	0.1	0.5	0.0	4.5
Squashes and soft drinks	1.3	1.2	1.7	0.1	0.0	0.0	4.2
Fruit juices	0.5	0.7	0.5	0.0	0.0	0.0	1.7
Other beverages	0.0	0.0	1.1	0.0	1.2	0.0	2.3
Confectionery	0.1	0.0	1.8	0.1	0.3	0.0	2.3
Vegetables and potatoes	0.3	0.2	0.9	0.0	0.0	0.0	1.4
Miscellaneous foods	0.7	0.6	0.5	0.2	0.2	0.0	2.1
Total family foods	**4.9**	**4.5**	**18.8**	**0.8**	**23.7**	**0.7**	**53.5**
Infants foods							
Infant formulas	0.0	0.0	0.1	0.2	6.0	0.7	7.0
Fruit juices and drinks	2.0	1.5	0.2	0.2	0.0	0.0	3.8
Prepared food in jar/can	0.6	0.8	1.3	0.0	0.5	0.0	3.3
Instant/dried foods	0.2	0.1	0.7	0.1	0.4	0.1	1.6
Rusks	0.1	0.0	0.9	0.0	0.0	0.0	1.1
Breast milk	0.0	0.0	0.0	0.0	1.3	0.0	1.3
Total infant food	**2.9**	**2.4**	**3.2**	**0.5**	**8.2**	**0.8**	**18.1**
Total food	**7.7**	**6.8**	**22.2**	**1.4**	**31.9**	**1.6**	**71.6**

Milk and milk products includes milks, ice-creams, creams and yoghurt but excludes cheese. Cereals and bread includes pasta, rice and breakfast cereals. Miscellaneous foods includes all meat, fish, cheese, eggs and products and dishes containing these; also fat spreads, nuts and nut spreads, preserves, honey, crisps and savoury snacks. Other beverages includes tea, coffee, cocoa, malted milk drink.

consumption of most sugars naturally incorporated in the cellular structure of foods (intrinsic sugars) represented a threat to health (DH, 1989b). Sugars not located within the cellular structure were described by COMA as extrinsic sugars. These are involved in the aetiology of dental caries. The COMA panel considered that milk without added sugars was not cariogenic as it contained factors which may protect against dental caries (DH, 1989b).

Non-milk extrinsic sugars (NMES) were estimated from average intakes of individual sugars from the food groups. For the purpose of this survey sucrose added to foods during manufacture, preparation and at the table and all the sugars in fruit juices, squashes and drinks were classed as non-milk extrinsic sugars. All the sugars in honey and the glucose in foods which contain glucose syrups were also classed as non-milk extrinsic sugars. Lactose and galactose were taken as intrinsic and milk sugars. The sugars in unsweetened fruit purees have been assumed to be intrinsic.

The average daily intake of non-milk extrinsic sugars was 24.7g for infants aged 6–12 months. Non-milk extrinsic sugars provided 9% and 12% of total energy for younger and older infants respectively. This compares with an intake of 18% of energy from 'added sugars' for the youngest pre-school children in a DH survey in 1968–9

(DHSS, 1975). Although the age groups are not directly comparable (the DHSS sample was 6–18 month old children and 20 years previously), it does suggest that intakes of NMES may be lower now than in the past. Indeed in our survey over half of the mothers who prepared milk based drinks for their infants and two thirds who fed breakfast cereals reported that they did not add further sugar to them. Drinks e.g. infant fruit drinks and squashes, were the main sources of NMES (Tables 9.16 and 9.17). The frequency of consumption of NMES is also an important factor in the aetiology of dental caries (DH, 1989b). Infants may well be offered fruit drinks and squashes in feeding beakers or bottles frequently throughout the day. If this practice is followed it may be damaging to teeth.

The Dietary Reference Value for non-milk extrinsic sugars as a percentage of food energy should not exceed 11% (DH, 1991). This is an average figure for the whole of the UK population and is therefore not just for infants. The average intake of non-milk extrinsic sugars for the older infants (9–12 months) was above the DRV.

Table 9.16 **The contribution of various food groups to the sugar content of the diets of infants aged 6–9 months (n=258)**

	Non-milk extrinsic sugars (g/day)	Intrinsic plus milk sugars (g/day)
Family foods		
Milk and milk products	1.9	11.6
Fruit	0.2	3.5
Biscuits, cakes and puddings	1.5	0.8
Cereals and bread	1.5	0.8
Squashes and soft drinks	1.1	0.0
Fruit juices	0.7	0.0
Other beverages	0.3	0.4
Confectionery	0.8	0.1
Vegetables and potatoes	0.4	0.3
Miscellaneous foods	0.8	0.4
Total family foods	**9.2**	**17.9**
Infant foods		
Infant formulas	0.8	20.7
Infant juices/drinks	5.5	0.0
Infant foods tin/jar	0.9	5.1
Infant foods, dried	2.5	2.1
Rusks	1.7	0.3
Breast milk	0.0	5.0
Total infant foods	**11.4**	**33.2**
Total food	**20.6**	**51.1**

Milk and milk products includes milks, ice-creams, creams and yoghurt but excludes cheese. Cereals and bread includes pasta, rice and breakfast cereals. Miscellaneous foods includes all meat, fish, cheese, eggs and products and dishes containing these; also fat spreads, nuts and nut spreads, preserves, honey, crisps and savoury snacks. Other beverages includes tea, coffee, cocoa, malted milk drinks.

Table 9.17 The contribution of various food groups to the sugar content of the diets of infants aged 9–12 months (n=230)

	Non-milk extrinsic sugars (g/day)	Intrinsic plus milk sugars (g/day)
Family foods		
Milk and milk products	4.3	21.4
Fruit	0.2	3.9
Biscuits, cakes and puddings	3.8	1.3
Cereals and bread	3.0	1.4
Squashes and soft drinks	4.2	0.0
Fruit juices	1.7	0.0
Other beverages	1.1	1.2
Confectionery	2.0	0.3
Vegetables and potatoes	0.8	0.6
Miscellaneous foods	1.7	0.6
Total family foods	**22.8**	**30.7**
Infant foods		
Infant formulas	0.3	6.7
Juices/drinks	3.8	0.0
Prepared infant foods jar/can	0.5	2.8
Infant foods, dried	0.9	0.7
Rusks	1.0	0.1
Breast milk	0.0	1.3
Total infant foods	**6.5**	**11.6**
Total food	**29.3**	**42.3**

Milk and milk products includes milks, ice-creams, creams and yoghurt but excludes cheese. Cereals and bread includes pasta, rice and breakfast cereals. Miscellaneous foods includes all meat, fish, cheese, eggs and products and dishes containing these; also fat spreads, nuts and nut spreads, preserves, honey, crisps and savoury snacks. Other beverages includes tea, coffee, cocoa, malted milk drinks.

Starch

The average daily intake of starch was significantly greater (p<0.01) for infants aged 9–12 months (46.6g, median 45.5g) compared with those aged 6–9 months (37.4g, median 35.9g). Amongst the older infants, males had on average significantly higher (p<0.01) intakes than females (49.5g and 44.4g respectively). These differences resulted in their significantly greater carbohydrate intakes.

Commercial infant foods were the main source of starch for infants aged 6–9 months providing on average 48% of the total compared with 18% for infants aged 9–12 months. The older infants (9–12 months) obtained twice the amount of starch from 'family foods' (37.5g) such as cereals (breakfast cereals, bread, biscuits, cakes and puddings) and vegetables compared to the younger infants (18.7g).

Dietary fibre (expressed as non-starch polysaccharides)

The average daily intake of dietary fibre (non-starch polysaccharides was significantly greater (p<0.01) for infants aged 9–12 months (4.8g, median 4.5g) compared with those aged 6–9 months (3.6g, median 3.4g). Males tended to have higher intakes than females, but this difference was significant (p<0.025) only in the

Table 9.18   Contribution of main foods to average daily intake of dietary fibre (g) by age

	Infants 6–9 months amount	%	Infants 9–12 months amount	%	Total sample amount	%
Cereal products of which	1.2	34	2.2	47	1.7	41
—breakfast cereals	0.8	21	1.3	27	1.0	24
—bread	0.3	9	0.7	14	0.5	12
Milk and milk products	0.0	0	0.0	0	0.0	0
Egg and egg dishes	0.0	0	0.0	0	0.0	0
Fat spreads	0.0	0	0.0	0	0.0	0
Meat and products	0.1	4	0.2	4	0.1	4
Fish and fish products	0.0	0	0.0	0	0.0	0
Vegetables of which	0.6	17	1.3	26	0.9	22
—potatoes	0.2	5	0.4	8	0.3	7
—vegetables	0.4	11	0.8	17	0.6	14
Fruits and nuts	0.2	6	0.3	6	0.3	6
Confectionery and preserves	0.0	0	0.0	0	0.0	0
Miscellaneous foods	0.1	2	0.1	2	0.1	2
Commercial infant foods of which	1.3	37	0.7	14	1.0	25
—foods in jars/cans	0.5	15	0.3	7	0.5	11
—instant/dried foods	0.6	17	0.2	4	0.4	10
—rusks	0.2	5	0.1	2	0.1	4
Infant formulas	0.0	0	0.0	0	0.0	0
Breast milk	0.0	0	0.0	0	0.0	0
Total	**3.6**	**100**	**4.8**	**100**	**4.2**	**100**
Number of cases	258		230		488	

younger infants (males 3.8g, median 3.6g and females 3.4g, median 3.2g).

'Family foods' provided most of the dietary fibre contributing 86% to the total intake of infants aged 9–12 months compared to 63% in the younger infants. Important sources for all infants aged 6–12 months were commercial infant food including rusks (25%), breakfast cereals (24%), vegetables (14%), bread (12%), potatoes (7%) and fruit (6%). Contributions of foods to average daily fibre intakes are shown in Table 9.18.

Fat

The average daily intake of total fat was 32.9g for infants aged 6–9 months (median 31.8g) and 38.6g for those aged 9–12 months (median 34.1g). These differences by age group were statistically significant (p<0.01).

Fat provided 37% of the total energy for infants aged 6–12 months which is lower than has previously been reported for British infants (McKillop and Durnin, 1982). There was little difference between the two age groups; the younger infants (6–9 months) derived 36% of their total energy from fat whereas the older infants (9–12 months) obtained on average 37%.

The contributions of the main food types to the intake of total fat varied between the two age groups and are shown in Table 9.19. Fifty-nine per cent of the total fat was provided by milks and dairy products. Infant formulas were the main source of fat in the diet of younger infants providing 29% of the total, whereas infants aged 9–12 months obtained more fat from cows milk (38%). Excluding cows milk, 'family foods' provided a quarter of the total fat intake for infants 6–9 months compared to 47% in the older infants. Fat spreads, meat and meat products, eggs and dishes made with egg, and cereal products such as cakes, biscuits and puddings, made marked contributions to the fat intake.

Fat intakes were significantly greater (p<0.01) for infants aged 9–12 months from the C2DE socioeconomic group (39.6g, median 39.1g) compared with those of a similar age from ABC1 socioeconomic

Table 9.19   Contribution of main food types to average daily fat (g) intake by age

	Infants 6–9 months		Infants 9–12 months		Total sample	
	amount	%	amount	%	amount	%
Cereal products of which	2.3	7	4.8	12	3.5	10
—biscuits	0.6	2	1.5	4	1.0	3
—cakes, buns and puddings	0.8	2	1.8	5	1.3	3.5
Milk and milk products of which	9.0	27	16.2	42	12.4	35
—cows milk	8.3	25	14.7	38	11.4	32
—cheese and cheese dishes	0.5	1	1.1	3	0.7	2
—yogurt	0.1	0	0.3	1	0.2	1
Egg and egg dishes	1.2	4	2.2	6	1.7	5
Fat spreads	1.2	4	2.9	7	2.0	6
Meat and meat products of which	1.3	4	2.7	7	2.0	6
—meat, meat dishes and products	1.1	3	2.5	6	1.7	5
—poultry and poultry dishes	0.2	1	0.2	1	0.2	1
Fish and fish products	0.2	1	0.5	1	0.3	1
Vegetables of which	0.2	1	1.0	3	0.6	2
—potatoes including chips	0.1	0	0.4	1	0.2	1
—savoury snacks	0.0	0	0.4	1	0.2	1
Fruits and nuts	0.1	0	0.1	0	0.1	0
Confectionery and preserves	0.4	1	0.7	2	0.5	1
Beverages	0.3	1	1.0	3	0.6	2
Miscellaneous foods	0.4	1	0.6	2	0.5	1
Commercial infant foods of which	3.8	12	2.0	5	3.0	8
—foods in jars/cans	1.7	5	1.2	3	1.5	4
—instant/dried foods	1.5	5	0.5	1	1.1	3
—rusks	0.6	2	0.3	1	0.4	1
Infant formulas	9.5	29	3.2	8	6.5	18
Breast milk	3.0	9	0.8	2	2.0	6
Total	**32.9**	**100**	**38.6**	**100**	**35.6**	**100**
Numbers of cases	258		230		488	

group (36.2g, median 36.4g). This difference was largely due to greater intakes of infant formulas. However, the percentage of energy derived from fat was similar irrespective of socioeconomic groups (37%).

Among the older infants, those with siblings had significantly greater fat intakes (p<0.05) compared to infants who were the only child in the family (39.5g, median 38.2g; and 36.8g, median 36.1g respectively). The difference was largely due to a greater consumption of 'family foods' such as fat spreads, cakes, puddings, biscuits, meat and meat products. Fat provided 38% of total energy for infants with siblings compared to 37% for those who were the only infant in the family.

Infants from SE, E Anglia and London had significantly lower fat intakes than those from both Wales, SW and the Midlands (p<0.01) and from Scotland and Northern England (p<0.05). The difference was due to a lower consumption of 'family foods' in the South Eastern region of England.

Fatty acids

Fatty acid data were available for all the major contributors to fat intake of infants (dairy products, cereal products, infant formulas and commercial infant foods, fat spreads and eggs). However, although cooking method (e.g. grilling and frying) was recorded, details of the type of fat used for frying was not collected. This approach was adopted because it was envisaged that few infants would be consuming fried foods in large quantities, and also, it was considered to be impractical to collect this information in the structured diary. All fried foods have been assumed to be fried in blended vegetable oil.

Fried foods were not a major source of fat in the diets of infants aged 6–12 months. For example, chips contributed less than 1% of the average intake. Thus the error in average fatty acid intake associated with the approach adopted for estimating average fatty acids from fried foods is unlikely to be large.

Saturated fatty acids

Infants aged 9–12 months had significantly greater (p<0.01) intakes of saturated fatty acids (19.5g, median 19.4g) compared with the younger infants (15.9g, median 15.6g). Intakes of saturated fatty acids were similar for males and females.

Saturated fatty acids represented a greater percentage of energy for the older infants (19%) compared with those aged 6–9 months (17%), however this difference was not significant.

Milks were the main source of saturated fatty acids. Infants aged 6–9 months obtained 28% from infant formulas and a further 33% from cows milk. Cows milk provided 48% and infant formulas 7% in the diets of older infants (9–12 months). Other 'family foods' which contributed to saturated fatty acids intake were similar to those which were important sources of fat, i.e. fat spreads (5%), egg and egg dishes (4%), cakes and puddings (4%) and meat and meat products (4%).

Among infants aged 9–12 months, saturated fatty acid intake was significantly greater (p<0.025) for those from the C2DE socioeconomic group (mean 20.1g, median 19.9g) compared with infants from ABC1 socioeconomic group (18.3g, median 18.6g). However, saturated fatty acids provided a similar proportion (19%) to the total energy intakes in both socioeconomic groups. Infants from the C2DE socioeconomic group derived more saturated fatty acids from infant formulas and chocolate and less from cheese and breast milk compared with those from the ABC1 socioeconomic group.

Infants from the SE, E Anglia and London had significantly lower intakes of saturated fatty acids than those from both Wales, the Midlands and SW (p<0.01) and from Scotland and Northern England (p<0.05). There was no regional difference in the contribution that saturated fatty acids made to total energy intakes.

Monounsaturated fatty acids

Infants aged 9–12 months consumed on average significantly more (p<0.01) monounsaturated fatty acids (11.9g, median 11.5g) compared with the younger infants (9.8g, median 9.7g). Intakes were similar for both sexes.

The foods which contributed most to the intake of monounsaturated fatty acids for infants aged 6–9 months and those aged 9–12 months were cows milk (23% and 33% respectively), infant formulas (28% and 7% respectively) and breast milk (9% and 2% respectively). Other important sources in the diets of infants aged 6–12 months were meat and meat products (7%), breast milk especially for those aged 6–9 months (7%), fat spreads (6%), egg and egg dishes (6%), commercial infant food (prepared in jars or cans 5%, dried 3%), cakes and puddings (5%) and biscuits (4%).

Amongst infants aged 9–12 months, those from the C2DE socioeconomic group consumed on average more (p<0.025) monounsaturated fatty acids (12.2g, median 11.8g) compared to those from the ABC1 socioeconomic group (11.3g, median 11.1g) due to higher intakes of infant formulas and chocolate confectionery.

Infants from Wales, the Midlands and SW had significantly greater intakes of monounsaturated fatty acids (p<0.025) (mean 11.3g, median 11.0g) than those from SE, E Anglia and London (mean 10.4g, median 10.1g).

Infants aged 9–12 months with siblings had significantly greater intakes of monounsaturated fatty acids (p<0.025) than infants who were the only child in the family (mean 12.3g, median 11.9g; and mean 11.2g, median 11.1g respectively). This difference was largely due to greater consumption of 'family foods'.

Polyunsaturated fatty acids

The average intake of polyunsaturated fatty acids was significantly higher (p<0.01) in the older infants (3.8g, median 3.5g) compared with the younger infants (3.2g, median 2.8g). Intakes of polyunsaturated fatty acids were similar for both males and females and for both socioeconomic groups.

Polyunsaturated fatty acids contributed 3.6% to the total energy intake. The polyunsaturated fatty acid to saturated fatty acid ratio (P:S ratio) was 0.2 (males 0.2, females 0.19). The P:S ratio amongst adults was double that of infants (men 0.4, females 0.38) (Gregory et al., 1990). This difference is largely due to the infants' greater dependency on milks which are rich in saturated fatty acids.

Important food sources of polyunsaturated fatty acids were infant formula (18%) especially amongst infants aged 6–9 months, commercial infant food (14%), cows milk (11%), fat spreads (10%), and meat and meat products (5%).

Intakes of polyunsaturated fatty acids were significantly higher ($p<0.01$) for infants aged 9–12 months with siblings than those who were the only child present in the family (4.0g, median 3.6g; and 3.5g, median 3.3g respectively).

Cholesterol

The average intake of cholesterol was significantly greater ($p<0.01$) for infants aged 9–12 months (184mg, median 170mg), compared with those aged 6–9 months (149mg, median 142mg). Intakes were similar for both sexes and socioeconomic groups.

The main sources were cows milk (25%), egg and egg dishes (25%), commercial infant foods (20%) and infant formulas (6%).

Vitamin A

Vitamin A can be obtained from the diet in two forms: preformed vitamin A (largely retinol) and carotenoids, chiefly B-carotene, which can be converted in the body to retinol. The total vitamin A content of the diet is expressed as retinol equivalent using the widely accepted conversion factor for carotene that 6μg is nutritionally equivalent to 1μg retinol (FAO/WHO, 1967).

Intakes of vitamin A were skewed and therefore all statistical tests have been performed using log transformations.

Retinol

Infants aged 6–9 months had an average intake of retinol from food (preformed vitamin A) of 611μg (median 516μg) compared with an average value for the older infants (9–12 months) of 547μg (median 390μg). Amongst males, average intakes were significantly greater ($p<0.025$) for infants aged 6–9 months (621μg, median 519μg) than the older infants (505μg, median 391μg).

Over one third (34%) of the intake of retinol for the entire sample was derived from infant formulas, 23% from cows milk and milk products and 17% from meat and meat products, largely liver and foods containing liver (Table 9.20).

Table 9.20 Contribution of the main food types to average daily intake of retinol (µg) by age

	Infants 6–9 months amount	%	Infants 9–12 months amount	%	Total sample amount	%
Cereal products	10	2	19	3	14	2
Milk and milk products	98	16	175	32	134	23
Egg and egg dishes	18	3	31	6	24	4
Fat spreads	12	2	28	5	19	3
Meat and meat products of which	62	10	134	24	96	17
—offal and offal dishes	59	10	124	23	89	15
Fish and fish products	0	0	1	0	1	0
Vegetables	0	0	0	0	0	0
Fruits and nuts	0	0	0	0	0	0
Confectionery and preserves	0	0	0	0	0	0
Beverages	4	1	11	2	7	1
Miscellaneous foods	0	0	0	0	0	0
Commercial infant foods of which	71	12	43	8	58	10
—foods in jars/cans	17	3	23	4	20	3
—instant/dried foods	51	8	19	3	36	6
—rusks	3	0	1	0	2	0
Infant formulas	294	48	95	17	200	34
Breast milk	43	7	11	2	28	5
Total	**611**	**100**	**547**	**100**	**581**	**100**
Number of cases	258		230		488	

Carotene

The average daily intake of carotene for infants aged 9–12 months was 1191µg (median 936µg) which was significantly greater (p<0.05) than that recorded for infants aged 6–9 months (1028µg, median 794µg). Overall males had significantly greater (p<0.025) intake than females, however this difference was most apparent (p<0.01) in the younger infants (1173µg and 880µg respectively).

Almost half of the carotene intake of infants aged 6–12 months was provided by vegetables. Commercial infant foods and meat dishes, which may contain vegetables, were also important sources (20% and 17% of total respectively) (Table 9.21).

Total vitamin A (expressed as retinol equivalent)

One quarter of the vitamin A intake from food (i.e. excluding supplements) of infants aged 6–12 months was from carotene. Infants aged 6–12 months had average intakes of 765µg (median 670µg) of total vitamin A from food, expressed as retinol equivalents, which were well in excess of the RNI (350µg). Intakes were very variable but were significantly higher (p<0.025) for the younger infants (6–9 months) compared with infants aged 9–12 months (mean 783µg, median 733µg; and 745µg, median 593µg respectively), although this difference between the age groups only reached significance (p<0.05) in males (Table 9.22). The major food source

Table 9.21 Contribution of main food types to average daily intake of carotene (μg) by age

	Infants 6–9 months amount	%	Infants 9–12 months amount	%	Total sample amount	%
Cereal products	5	1	10	1	8	1
Milk and milk products	58	6	105	9	80	7
Egg and egg dishes	3	0	5	0	4	0
Fat spreads	4	0	9	1	6	1
Meat and meat products (includes dishes with carrots)	165	16	206	17	184	17
Fish and fish products	9	1	2	0	6	1
Vegetables	420	41	630	53	519	47
Fruits and nuts	5	1	7	1	6	1
Confectionery and preserves	0	0	1	0	1	0
Beverages	3	0	8	1	6	1
Miscellaneous foods	43	4	38	3	40	4
Commercial infant foods of which	281	27	160	13	224	20
—foods in jars/cans	174	17	123	10	150	14
—instant/dried foods	105	10	36	3	73	7
Infant formulas	31	3	10	1	21	2
Breast milk	0	0	0	0	0	0
Total	**1028**	**100**	**1191**	**100**	**1105**	**100**
Number of cases	258		230		488	

Table 9.22 Average daily intakes of retinol, carotene and retinol equivalent (μg) by age and sex

	Males 6–9 months	9–12 months	6–12 months	Females 6–9 months	9–12 months	6–12 months	Infants 6–12 months
Retinol							
Mean	621	505	571	602	576	589	581
Median	519	391	475	509	387	441	449
Lower 2.5%	172	110	140	166	146	158	157
Upper 2.5%	1507	1681	1581	1708	2533	1813	1707
SD	388	351	376	380	586	495	444
Number of infants	130	96	226	128	134	262	488
Carotene							
Mean	1173	1238	1201	880	1157	1021	1104
Median	875	968	903	692	908	812	829
Lower 2.5%	258	184	240	191	156	195	225
Upper 2.5%	3185	4837	3887	2214	3058	2805	3140
SD	891	1004	939	639	772	722	834
Number of infants	130	96	226	128	134	262	488
Retinol equivalent							
Mean	816	711	771	784	769	759	765
Median	733	593	685	678	617	655	670
Lower 2.5%	298	209	254	295	284	291	282
Upper 2.5%	1757	1840	1800	1871	2653	1976	1873
SD	404	396	403	389	605	510	463
Number of infants	130	96	226	128	134	262	488

was milk, either infant formulas for the younger infants or cows milks for those aged 9–12 months.

Supplement users

The Panel on Child Nutrition of the Committee on the Medical Aspects of Food Policy (DHSS, 1988) recommend that vitamin supplementation should be given to infants and young children aged from 6 months up to at least 2 years and preferably 5 years.

Just under half of the sample of infants aged 6–9 months (47%) were receiving vitamin supplements. Vitamin A intake from food was similar in supplement users to the overall mean intake of infants aged 6–9 months. Supplements provided an additional 165μg of vitamin A, representing on average 19% of total intake (948μg). Amongst supplement users average intake of total vitamin A from all sources was 271% of the RNI.

Among infants aged 9–12 months, 40% of the sample was receiving vitamin supplements. Food provided on average a similar quantity of total vitamin A in both supplement and non-supplement users. Supplements provided an additional 168μg contributing on average 21% to total intake of vitamin A for supplement users. Amongst supplement users intake was 262% of the RNI.

Vitamin D

Vitamin D intakes were skewed and therefore all statistical tests have been performed using log transformations.

Intakes from food
(Tables 9.23 and 9.24)

Average daily intakes of vitamin D from food alone for infants aged 6–12 months were 3.49μg (median 1.21μg), 50% of the RNI (7.0μg). Infants aged 6–9 months had markedly greater intakes ($p < 0.01$) than the older infants. Average daily intake from food for infants aged 6–9 months was 4.7μg (median 2.2μg) and that recorded for infants aged 9–12 months was 2.14μg (median 0.95μg). Infant formulas, which are fortified with vitamin D, were by far the major source.

There was no significant difference in intakes by sex or by socio-economic group or by presence of other children in the family. Infants from Scotland and Northern England had significantly greater ($p < 0.05$) vitamin D intakes compared with those from SE, E Anglia and London. This difference was largely due to the higher consumption of infant formulas in the North.

Table 9.23 Average daily intake of vitamin D (μg) by age, sex, socioeconomic group and region

	6–9 months	9–12 months	Infants 6–9 months ABC1	Infants 6–9 months C2DE	Wales, SW, Midlands	Scotland, N England	E Anglia, SE, London
Mean	4.70	2.14	4.22	4.96	3.39	3.91	3.12
Median	2.20	0.95	1.53	3.41	1.26	1.42	1.03
Lower 2.5%	0.14	0.16	0.08	0.22	0.20	0.20	0.11
Upper 2.5%	15.51	11.78	15.54	16.07	15.79	14.21	14.16
SD	4.79	3.30	4.87	4.74	4.43	4.35	4.25
Number of infants	258	230	91	167	149	178	161

Table 9.24 Contributions of main food types to average daily intake of vitamin D (μg) by age

	Infants 6–9 months		Infants 9–12 months		Total sample	
	amount	%	amount	%	amount	%
Cereal products of which	0.03	1	0.09	4	0.06	2
—breakfast cereals	0.01	0	0.04	2	0.03	1
—cakes, buns and puddings	0.02	0	0.05	2	0.03	1
Milk and milk products	0.08	2	0.18	8	0.13	4
Egg and egg products	0.09	2	0.15	7	0.12	3
Fat spreads	0.07	2	0.18	9	0.13	4
Meat and meat products	0.00	0	0.01	0	0.00	0
Fish and fish products	0.01	0	0.05	2	0.03	1
Vegetables	0.00	0	0.00	0	0.00	0
Fruits and nuts	0.00	0	0.00	0	0.00	0
Confectionery and preserves	0.00	0	0.00	0	0.00	0
Beverages	0.00	0	0.01	0	0.00	0
Miscellaneous foods	0.00	0	0.00	0	0.00	0
Commercial infant foods of which	0.52	11	0.20	9	0.37	11
—food in jars/cans	0.09	2	0.04	2	0.06	2
—instant/dried foods	0.38	8	0.14	7	0.27	8
—rusks	0.05	1	0.02	1	0.04	1
Infant formulas	3.87	82	1.27	59	2.65	76
Breast milk	0.01	0	0.00	0	0.00	0
Total	**4.7**	**100**	**2.1**	**100**	**3.5**	**100**
Number of cases	258		230		488	

Supplement users

Infants aged 6–9 months

Among infants aged 6–9 months 47% were receiving additional vitamin D from supplements. Average daily intake from food amongst supplement users was 4.2μg (median 1.7μg) with a further 5.8μg (median 7.0μg) from vitamin supplements. Supplements contributed on average 63% to their total intake. Amongst supplement users intakes met the RNI.

Infants aged 9–12 months

Supplements provided on average 5.9μg of vitamin D (median 7.0μg). This represents 77% of total vitamin D intake. Food contributed only 1.7μg (median 1.0μg) to the total intake of 7.6μg. Amongst supplement users, intake met the RNI.

Vitamin E

Average daily intakes of vitamin E were significantly greater (p<0.01) in the younger infants (4.5mg, median 3.7mg) compared with those aged 9–12 months (3.5mg, median 2.9mg) and this was largely due to the greater consumption of infant formula among infants aged 6–9 months. There were no significant differences in intakes by sex or regional group. Infants from the C2DE socioeconomic group tended to have greater intakes than those from ABC1 socioeconomic group but this difference was only significant (p<0.05) for infants aged 9–12 months.

Milks provided 58% of the total vitamin E intake in the younger infants compared to 33% amongst those aged 9–12 months. Besides milk, the older infants obtained over half of their total vitamin E from 'family foods' such as cereals (13%), fat spreads (9%), egg and egg dishes (7%), vegetables including potatoes (7%) and from savoury snacks (4%).

Vitamin C

Vitamin C intakes were skewed and therefore all statistical tests have been performed using log transformations.

Intakes from food (Tables 9.25 and 9.26)

The average daily intake of vitamin C from food was 100mg (median 81mg), four times the current RNI of 25mg. The high intakes were largely due to the high consumption of fortified commercial infant foods. The major food sources were commercial infant fruit drinks and juices, providing just over one third of the total intake for infants from both age groups.

Average intakes of vitamin C from food were significantly greater (p<0.01) for infants aged 6–9 months than for those aged 9–12 months (117mg, median 99mg; and 81mg, median 57mg respectively). Commercial infant foods and infant formulas provided 86% of food vitamin C for infants aged 6–9 months compared with 64% amongst those aged 9–12 months.

Among infants from both age groups, vitamin C intake (from food sources) for those fed solely commercial infant food were significantly greater (p<0.01) compared with those fed predominantly 'family foods' (see Chapter 13 for more details).

There was no significant difference between males and females in the average intake of vitamin C from food sources.

Irrespective of age, infants who were the only child in the family had higher intakes of vitamin C than infants with siblings. This difference was more marked (p<0.01) amongst the younger infants (mean 140mg, median 121mg; and mean 105mg, median 90mg respectively) than those aged 9–12 months (p<0.05) (mean 95mg, median 72mg for the only child; and mean 74mg, median 54mg for those with siblings), and was largely a result of higher intakes of fortified commercial infant food such as infant fruit juice drinks and desserts.

There were no significant differences in intakes by regional groups or by socioeconomic groups ABC1 and C2DE.

Supplement users

Infants aged 6–9 months
Among infants aged 6–9 months 47% were receiving vitamin supplements. Average vitamin C intake from food was 114mg. Supplements provided an additional 17mg for supplement users, which corresponded on average to 16% of their total intake.

Table 9.25 Average daily intakes of Vitamin C (mg) by age and sex

	6–9 months	9–12 months	6–12 months	6–9 months Only child	6–9 months Siblings	9–12 months Only child	9–12 months Siblings	Total Sample Wales, SW, Midlands	Total Sample Scotland, N England	Total Sample E Anglia, SE, London
Mean	117	81	99	140	105	95	74	87	103	109
Median	99	57	81	121	90	72	54	69	88	82
Lower 2.5%	19	15	15	14	19	15	15	16	17	15
Upper 2.5%	352	304	318	370	348	329	260	254	278	378
SD	81.9	73.3	79.9	87.1	76.6	81.1	68.5	61.2	77.7	95.0
Number of Infants	258	230	488	89	169	75	155	149	178	161

Table 9.26 Contribution of main food types to average daily intake of vitamin C (mg) by age

	Infants 6–9 months amount	%	Infants 9–12 months amount	%	Total sample amount	%
Cereal products	0.2	0	0.4	0	0.3	0
Milk and milk products	3.6	3	6.2	8	4.8	5
Egg and egg dishes	0.0	0	0.0	0	0.0	0
Fat spreads	0.0	0	0.0	0	0.0	0
Meat and meat products	0.4	0	0.6	1	0.5	1
Fish and fish products	0.0	0	0.0	0	0.0	0
Vegetables	2.9	3	5.6	7	4.2	4
of which						
—vegetables	2.0	2	3.6	4	2.7	3
—potatoes	0.9	1	1.9	2	1.4	1
—savoury snacks	0.0	0	0.1	0	0.1	0
Fruits and nuts	2.1	2	2.5	3	2.3	2
Confectionery and preserves	0.1	0	0.1	0	0.1	0
Beverages	4.2	4	12.6	16	8.2	8
of which						
—fruit juice	2.1	2	4.3	5	3.2	3
—soft drinks	1.9	2	7.9	10	4.7	5
Miscellaneous foods	0.0	0	0.0	0	0.0	0
Commercial infant foods	76.9	66	45.0	55	61.9	62
of which						
—foods in jars/cans	21.3	18	12.2	15	17.0	17
—instant/dried foods	14.5	12	4.8	6	9.9	10
—rusks	0.1	0	0.1	0	0.1	0
—infant fruit juice/drinks	41.0	35	27.9	34	37.8	35
Infant formulas	23.5	20	7.4	9	15.9	16
Breast milk	2.7	2	0.7	1	1.8	2
Total	**117**	**100**	**81**	**100**	**100**	**100**
Number of cases	258		230		488	

Infants aged 9–12 months

Among infants aged 9–12 months, 40% were receiving vitamin supplements. Intakes of vitamin C from food were 84mg with supplements providing an additional 17mg, on average contributing 24% to their total intake.

Thiamin

The average intake of thiamin was 1.10mg (median 1.04mg), well in excess of the RNI (0.2mg for infants aged 7–9 months; 0.3mg for infants aged 10–12 months).

Intakes of thiamin were significantly greater (p<0.01) for infants aged 6–9 months compared with those aged 9–12 months (1.16mg, median 1.12mg; and 1.03mg, median 0.93mg respectively).

Infants from socioeconomic group C2DE tended to have, on average, higher intakes than those from ABC1 socioeconomic group, largely as a result of greater intakes of infant formulas. This difference was only significant for infants aged 9–12 months (p<0.01) with those from socioeconomic group ABC1 having average intakes of 0.93mg (median 0.88mg) compared with 1.07mg (median 0.97mg) for infants from the C2DE socioeconomic group.

Infants from Scotland and Northern England consumed more infant formulas and thus had significantly greater (p<0.01) intakes of thiamin (1.15mg, median 1.10mg) than those from E Anglia, SE and London (1.05mg, median 1.02mg).

Among infants aged 6–9 months, those with siblings had significantly lower (p<0.025) thiamin intakes compared with infants who were the only child in the family.

Commercial infant foods provided one third of the average daily intake of thiamin for infants aged 6–12 months but within the sample their contribution declined with age from 40% for infants aged 6–9 months to 25% in the older infants. Milks were important sources of thiamin with infant formulas contributing 28% of the total intake in the younger infants whereas cows milks provided 21% for infants aged 9–12 months. Cereals, predominantly breakfast cereals which tend to be fortified, provided 10% of the total intake which is similar to the contribution they make in the diets of

Table 9.27 Contribution of main food types to average daily intake of thiamin (mg) by age

	Infants 6–9 months		Infants 9–12 months		Total sample	
	amount	%	amount	%	amount	%
Cereal products of which	0.13	11	0.25	23	0.17	16
—bread	0.03	2	0.06	5	0.04	4
—breakfast cereals	0.09	7	0.15	14	0.11	10
Milk and milk products	0.13	11	0.24	23	0.17	16
Eggs and egg dishes	0.01	1	0.01	1	0.01	1
Fat spreads	0.00	0	0.00	0	0.00	0
Meat and meat products	0.02	2	0.03	4	0.03	3
Fish and fish products	0.00	0	0.00	0	0.00	0
Vegetables of which	0.04	4	0.09	9	0.07	6
—potatoes	0.03	3	0.06	6	0.05	4
Fruits and nuts	0.01	1	0.01	1	0	1
Confectionery and preserves	0.00	0	0.00	0	0.00	0
Beverages	0.02	1	0.03	3	0.02	2
Miscellaneous foods	0.01	1	0.01	1	0.01	1
Commercial infant foods of which	0.47	40	0.25	25	0.37	33
—infant food in jar/can	0.24	20	0.17	17	0.21	19
—instant/dried food	0.18	15	0.06	5	0.12	11
—rusks	0.04	4	0.02	2	0.03	3
Infant formulas	0.32	28	0.10	10	0.22	20
Breast milk	0.01	1	0.00	0	0.01	1
Total	**1.16**	**100**	**1.03**	**100**	**1.10**	**100**
Number of cases	258		230			488

adults (12%) (Gregory et al., 1990). However, unlike adults, vegetables and meat contributed little to thiamin intakes for infants.

Riboflavin

The average intake of riboflavin for infants aged 6–9 months was 1.57mg (median 1.53mg) and 1.53mg (median 1.45mg) for infants aged 9–12 months. There was little variation in intake by sex or region (Table 9.28).

Infants from the C2DE socioeconomic group tended to have on average higher intakes than those from the socioeconomic group ABC1, although this difference was only significant ($p<0.05$) for infants aged 9–12 months (ABC1 mean 1.43mg, median 1.42mg; C2DE mean 1.57mg, median 1.46mg). Infants from the socioeconomic C2DE group obtained more riboflavin from infant formulas than did those from the ABC1 socioeconomic group.

The average intake was almost four times greater than the RNI.

Milks and milk products, predominantly infant formulas in the younger infants (6–9 months) and cows milk in infants aged 9–12

Table 9.28 Contribution of main food types to average daily intake of riboflavin (mg) by age

	Infants 6–9 months		Infants 9–12 months		Total sample	
	amount	%	amount	%	amount	%
Cereal products of which	0.10	7	0.20	13	0.15	10
—breakfast cereals	0.07	5	0.14	9	0.11	7
Milk and milk products	0.42	27	0.76	50	0.58	37
Eggs and egg dishes	0.03	2	0.05	3	0.04	3
Fat spreads	0.00	0	0.00	0	0.00	0
Meat and meat products of which	0.03	2	0.05	4	0.04	3
—beef, pork, lamb dishes and products	0.02	1	0.03	2	0.02	2
—offal dishes and products	0.01	1	0.02	1	0.02	1
Fish and fish products	0.00	0	0.01	0	0.00	0
Vegetables	0.01	1	0.01	1	0.01	1
Fruits and nuts	0.01	1	0.01	1	0.01	1
Preserves and confectionery	0.00	0	0.01	0	0.01	0
Beverages	0.02	1	0.05	3	0.03	2
Miscellaneous foods	0.01	1	0.02	1	0.01	1
Commercial infant foods of which	0.31	20	0.14	9	0.23	15
—foods in jars/cans	0.06	4	0.04	3	0.05	3
—instant/dried foods	0.17	11	0.05	4	0.11	7
—rusks	0.08	5	0.05	3	0.07	4
Infant formulas	0.60	38	0.20	13	0.41	26
Breast milk	0.02	1	0.01	0	0.01	1
Total	**1.6**	**100**	**1.5**	**100**	**1.5**	**100**
Number of cases	258		230		488	

months were the major source of riboflavin providing 63% of the total. Commercial infant foods (15%) and cereals, largely breakfast cereals (10%) (many of which are fortified), were other important sources in the diets of infants aged 6–12 months.

Niacin (niacin equivalent)
(Table 9.29)

Niacin is available preformed in foods and is also produced in the body from tryptophan, an amino acid. The niacin content is expressed as niacin equivalent which includes the contribution from tryptophan. It is usual to assume that 60mg of dietary tryptophan will be equivalent to 1mg of dietary niacin (Horwitt, 1956).

The average daily intake was similar in both age groups (6–9 months 12.48mg; 9–12 months 12.47mg), but overall was signficantly greater (p<0.01) for males (12.90mg, median 12.58mg) than females (12.10mg, median 11.60mg). Average niacin equivalent recorded in this survey were well in excess (280%) of the RNI for infants of this age.

Older infants from the C2DE socioeconomic group obtained on average 1.34mg of total niacin from infant formulas, which is twice the amount they provide in the diets of those from ABC1 socio-economic group (0.55mg). This accounts for the significantly greater niacin intakes (p<0.025) found in older infants from C2DE socio-economic group.

Fewer infants from Scotland and Northern England were receiving breast milk and more were fed infant formulas compared with those from SE, E Anglia and London. This difference in feeding patterns contributed to the significantly greater total niacin intakes (p<0.05) amongst those from Scotland and Northern England (12.66mg, median 12.46mg) compared with infants from SE, E Anglia and London (12.05mg, median 11.46mg).

The major sources of total niacin were milks, predominantly infant formulas for infants aged 6–9 months (28%) and cows milk (28%) amongst the older infants. The contributions made by foods to the total intake of niacin varied considerably between infants from the two age groups. Infants aged 6–9 months obtained 26% from commercial infant foods. A greater proportion of total niacin came from 'family foods' in the older infants (50%) compared with 27% in infants aged 6–9 months. Infants aged 9–12 months obtained 16%· from cereals of which half was from breakfast cereals which may be fortified with the vitamin, and 13% from meat and meat products (Table 9.29).

Folate
(Table 9.30)

The intakes of folate showed little variation with age, region, socioeconomic group or whether siblings were present in the family or not. Overall however, males had a significantly greater (p<0.01) average folate intake than females (110µg, median 107µg; and 102µg, median 97µg respectively). The average intake (106µg) was over twice the RNI (50µg).

64

Table 9.29 Contribution of main food types to average daily intake of niacin equivalent (mg) by age

	Infants 6–9 months amount	%	Infants 9–12 months amount	%	Total sample Amount	%
Cereal products of which	1.0	8	1.9	16	1.4	12
—breakfast cereals	0.6	4	1.1	8	0.8	6
—bread	0.2	2	0.5	4	0.3	3
Milk and milk products	2.2	18	4.0	32	3.1	25
Eggs and egg dishes	0.2	2	0.4	3	0.3	3
Fat spreads	0.0	0	0.0	0	0.0	0
Meat and meat products of which	1.0	8	1.6	13	1.3	10
—beef, pork, lamb dishes and products	0.7	5	1.2	10	0.9	7
—poultry dishes and products	0.3	2	0.3	3	0.3	2
Fish and fish products	0.2	1	0.3	2	0.2	2
Vegetables	0.3	2	0.7	5	0.5	4
Fruits and nuts	0.1	1	0.2	1	0.1	1
Preserves and confectionery	0.0	0	0.0	0	0.0	0
Beverages	0.1	1	0.3	2	0.2	2
Miscellaneous foods	0.1	1	0.2	2	0.2	1
Commercial infant foods of which	3.2	26	1.5	13	2.4	20
—foods in jars/cans	0.8	7	0.6	5	0.7	6
—instant/dried foods	1.8	14	0.6	5	1.2	10
—rusks	0.6	5	0.3	3	0.5	4
Infant formulas	3.5	28	1.1	9	2.3	19
Breast milk	0.5	4	0.1	1	0.3	3
Total	**12.5**	**100**	**12.5**	**100**	**12.5**	**100**
Number of cases	258		230		488	

Commercial infant foods were the main source of folate amongst the younger infants (6–9 months) providing 27%, whereas cows milk made the greatest contribution in the older infants (22%) (Table 9.30).

Vitamin B$_6$

Average daily intakes of vitamin B$_6$ (pyridoxine) were similar in both age groups; 0.82mg (median 0.83mg) for infants aged 6–9 months and 0.84mg (median 0.79mg) for the older infants. Overall males had significantly greater (p<0.01) intakes than females (0.86mg, median 0.85mg; and 0.80mg, median 0.76mg respectively). Average intakes were well in excess of the RNI (0.3mg infants aged 7–9 months; 0.4mg infants aged 10–12 months).

A range of foods contributed to vitamin B$_6$ intake of infants aged 6–12 months. These included milk and milk products (22%), infant formulas (21%), commercial infant food (15%) and vegetables including potatoes (8%). Ten per cent of the average intake of vitamin B$_6$ was provided by breakfast cereals, many of which are fortified. Table 9.31 shows contributions of food types to average intakes of vitamin B$_6$.

Table 9.30 Contribution of main food types to average daily intake of folate (µg) by age

	Infants 6–9 months amount	%	Infants 9–12 months amount	%	Total sample amount	%
Cereal products of which	9	9	17	16	13	12
—breakfast cereals	5	4	8	7	6	6
—bread	3	3	6	5	4	4
Milk and milk products of which	16	15	30	28	22	21
—yogurt	2	2	5	5	3	3
Eggs and egg dishes	3	3	5	5	4	4
Fat spreads	0	0	0	0	0	0
Meat and meat products of which	3	3	5	5	4	4
—offal and offal dishes	1	1	1	1	1	1
Fish and fish products	0	0	1	1	1	1
Vegetables of which	9	9	19	17	14	13
—vegetables	5	5	9	9	7	7
—potatoes	5	4	9	8	7	6
Fruits and nuts	2	2	2	2	2	2
Confectionery and preserves	0	0	0	0	0	0
Beverages	2	2	4	4	3	3
Miscellaneous foods	2	2	2	2	2	2
Commercial infant foods of which	29	27	13	12	21	20
—foods in jars/cans	10	9	6	6	8	8
—instant/dried foods	18	17	6	6	12	12
—rusks	1	1	1	1	1	1
Infant formulas	26	25	8	8	17	17
Breast milk	4	4	1	1	2	2
Total	**104**	**100**	**107**	**100**	**106**	**100**
Number of cases	258		230		488	

Vitamin B$_{12}$

Average daily intakes of vitamin B$_{12}$ were significantly greater (p<0.01) in the older infants (3.4µg, median 3.2µg) compared with those aged 6–9 months (3.0µg, median 2.9µg), but were similar in males and females and across regions. Amongst the younger infants, those from the C2DE socioeconomic group had significantly greater (p<0.025) intakes of vitamin B$_{12}$ (3.1µg) than those from ABC1 socioeconomic group (2.8µg). There was no marked difference in vitamin B$_{12}$ intake by socioeconomic group in the older infants. Average intake of vitamin B$_{12}$ was eight times the RNI. Vitamin B$_{12}$ has extremely low toxicity and no toxic effects other than 'rare allergic reactions' have been encountered in man (DH, 1991).

Overall, cows milk and milk products provided 40% of the total intake of vitamin B$_{12}$, infant formulas 18%, commercial infant foods 15%, eggs and egg dishes 7%, and offal containing dishes 5%. Table 9.31 shows contributions of food types to average intakes of vitamin B$_{12}$.

Table 9.31 Contribution of food types to average daily intake of vitamins B$_{12}$, B$_6$, pantothenic acid and biotin

| | Vitamin B$_{12}$ | | | | Vitamin B$_6$ | | | |
| | Infants 6–9 months | | Infants 9–12 months | | Infants 6–9 months | | Infants 9–12 months | |
	µg	%	µg	%	mg	%	mg	%
Commercial infant foods	0.62	21	0.34	10	0.16	20	0.08	9
Breast milk	0.00	0	0.00	0	0.01	1	0.00	0
Infant formulas	0.84	28	0.27	8	0.26	32	0.08	10
Cows milk	0.88	30	1.58	46	0.13	16	0.24	28
'Family foods'	0.64	21	1.21	36	0.26	31	0.45	53
Total intake	**3.0**	**100**	**3.4**	**100**	**0.82**	**100**	**0.84**	**100**
Number of cases	258		230		258		230	

| | Pantothenic acid | | | | Biotin | | | |
| | Infants 6–9 months | | Infants 9–12 months | | Infants 6–9 months | | Infants 9–12 months | |
	mg	%	mg	%	µg	%	µg	%
Commercial infant foods	0.96	24	0.39	11	4.05	15	1.83	8
Breast milk	0.18	5	0.05	1	0.74	3	0.19	1
Infant formulas	1.40	36	0.43	12	12.10	46	4.33	18
Cows milk	0.67	17	1.20	34	4.44	17	7.98	33
'Family foods'	0.72	18	1.44	41	5.19	20	9.53	40
Total intake	**3.9**	**100**	**3.5**	**100**	**26.5**	**100**	**23.8**	**100**
Number of cases	258		230		258		230	

Pantothenic acid

Infants aged 6–9 months had significantly greater (p<0.01) average daily intakes of pantothenic acid (3.9mg, median 3.7mg) than the older infants (3.5mg, median 3.2mg). Overall males had significantly (p<0.05) greater intakes than females (3.9mg, median 3.6mg; and 3.7mg, median 3.4mg respectively).

The main sources of pantothenic acid in the diets of infants aged 6–12 months were milks, either infant formulas (25%) or cows milk (25%), and commercial infant foods (19%). Table 9.31 shows the contributions of food types to average intakes of pantothenic acid.

Biotin

Average intakes of biotin were greater for the younger infants (26.5µg, median 22.0µg) than infants aged 9–12 months (23.8µg, median 21.3µg) although this difference was not significant.

Within the total sample of infants important sources of biotin were infant formulas (33%), cows milk (24%), commercial infant foods (12%), cereals (11%) especially breakfast cereals (6%) and eggs and egg dishes (8%). Table 9.31 shows the contributions of food types to average intakes of biotin.

Minerals

Average intakes of all minerals except copper were significantly greater (p<0.01) for infants aged 9–12 months than for infants aged 6–9 months. Males had greater intakes than females and these differences were significant for potassium (p<0.025), zinc (p<0.05), and manganese (p<0.01) in the younger infants (6–9 months) and magnesium (p<0.05), copper (p<0.05), iron (p<0.05) and manganese (p<0.05) in infants aged 9–12 months (Table 9.32). Average intakes for all minerals exceeded the RNI with the exception of zinc (90% of the RNI).

Table 9.32 Average daily intake of minerals by age

	Units	Infants aged 6–9 months			Infants aged 9–12 months			Total sample		
		Mean	Median	SD	Mean	Median	SD	Mean	Median	SD
Sodium	mg	589	548	276	943	898	341	756	705	355
Potassium	mg	1239	1214	335	1479	1438	379	1352	1340	376
Magnesium	mg	111	108	35	140	136	38	124	125	39
Phosphorus	mg	668	650	222	824	821	236	742	739	241
Copper	mg	0.6	0.5	0.2	0.6	0.5	0.2	0.6	0.5	0.2
Chloride	mg	959	869	416	1479	1418	517	1205	1125	533
Iodine	μg	176	164	74	235	236	85	204	196	85
Manganese	mg	1.1	1.0	0.5	1.2	1.1	0.5	1.2	1.1	0.5
Number of infants		258			230			488		

The contribution that food types made to the total intake of selected minerals (sodium, chloride, potassium, magnesium, phosphorus, copper, iodine and manganese) in the diets of infants aged 6–9 months and 9–12 months is shown in Table 9.33. Calcium, iron and zinc are presented in separate sections of the report.

The addition of salt at the table or during cooking was not quantified therefore sodium intakes are likely to be higher than recorded in this study. (For information on the addition of salt to selected foods see page 20).

Within 'family foods', cereals, notably bread and breakfast cereals made an important contribution to the intakes of minerals especially sodium (26%), chloride (23%), magnesium (21%) and manganese (42%) for infants aged 6–12 months.

Calcium

Average intakes of calcium were significantly lower (p<0.01) among the younger infants (744mg, median 718mg) compared with the older infants (825mg, median 809mg), but intakes of both groups were well in excess of the RNI (Table 9.34). For both age groups there were no significant differences with socioeconomic groups, presence of other children in the family or between those fed predominantly commercial infant food and 'family foods'. There was little regional variation. Calcium intakes were similar among infants from Wales, Midlands and SW (mean 796mg; median 774mg) and Scotland and Northern England (mean 799mg; median 807mg). Infants from the SE, E Anglia and London obtained less calcium from infant formulas and 'family foods' compared to those from the

Table 9.34 Average daily calcium intake (mg) by age and sex

	Infants aged 6–9 months			Infants aged 9–12 months			Infants aged 6–12 months		
	Males	Females	All	Males	Females	All	Males	Females	All
Mean	760	729	744	849	808	825	797	769	783
Median	752	676	718	814	799	809	789	751	767
Lower 2.5%	347	299	334	346	313	326	354	309	334
Upper 2.5%	1318	1503	1310	1494	1589	1501	1425	1525	1433
SD	236	254	245	269	271	270	254	265	260
Number of infants	130	128	258	96	134	230	226	262	488

Table 9.33 Contribution of food types to total intakes of selected minerals for infants aged 6–9 months and 9–12 months

	Units	Infants aged 6–9 months (n=258)						Infants aged 9–12 months (n=230)					
		Total	Commercial infant food	Breast milk	Infant formulas	Cows milk	'Family foods'	Total	Commercial infant food	Breast milk	Infant formulas	Cows milk	'Family foods'
Sodium*	mg	**589**	99	11	73	125	280	**943**	52	3	23	224	641
Potassium	mg	**1239**	278	43	224	322	372	**1479**	129	11	71	581	687
Magnesium	mg	**111**	25	2	17	27	39	**140**	11	1	6	50	72
Phosphorus*	mg	**668**	160	11	119	205	173	**824**	71	3	37	370	343
Copper	mg	**0.6**	0.29	0.03	0.05	0.03	0.17	**0.6**	0.16	0.01	0.02	0.06	0.34
Chloride	mg	**959**	148	31	131	215	435	**1479**	79	8	41	384	967
Iodine**	µg	**176**	18	5	38	82	33	**235**	9	1	12	146	66
Manganese	mg	**1.1**	0.47	0.00	0.04	0.00	0.56	**1.2**	0.21	0.00	0.02	0.00	1.02

*The use of table salt was not quantified.

**Iodine values of cows milk as winter milk which are higher than in milk collected in the summer.

Table 9.35 Contribution of main food types to average daily intake of calcium (mg) by age

	Infants 6–9 months amount	%	Infants 9–12 months amount	%	Total sample amount	%
Cereal products of which	37	5	71	9	53	7
—bread	7	1	17	2	12	1
Milk products of which	291	39	537	65	407	52
—milk	254	34	457	55	349	45
—yogurt	29	4	59	7	43	5
—cheese	9	1	21	3	15	2
Egg and egg dishes	5	1	9	1	7	1
Fat spreads	0	0	0	0	0	0
Meat and meat products	3	0	6	1	5	1
Fish and fish products	2	0	5	1	3	0
Vegetables	5	1	11	1	8	1
Fruit and nuts	1	0	2	0	2	0
Confectionery and preserves	3	0	6	1	5	1
Beverages	11	1	31	4	21	3
Miscellaneous foods	3	0	5	1	4	1
Commercial infant foods of which	201	27	85	10	146	19
—foods in jars/cans	34	5	21	3	28	3
—instant/dried foods	131	17	44	5	90	11
—rusks	34	5	19	2	27	3
Infant formulas	155	21	49	6	105	13
Breast milk	25	3	6	1	16	2
Total	**742**	**100**	**825**	**100**	**783**	**100**
Number of cases	258		230		488	

other regional groups and had considerably lower average intakes (mean 752mg; median 758mg). This difference was only significant (p<0.05) when compared with infants from Scotland and Northern England.

Contributions made by different food groups to the total intake of calcium for the different age groups and the total sample are shown in Table 9.35. Milks were the major source of calcium in the diets of infants but the contribution made by infant formulas and cows milk varied between the two age groups. Infants aged 6–9 months, obtained 21% of their total calcium from infant formulas with a further 34% from cows milk, while in the older infants cows milk contributed 55% and infant formulas 6%.

Iron

Iron intakes were skewed and therefore all statistical tests have been performed using log transformations.

The average daily intake of iron for infants aged 6–12 months was 8.1mg, slightly above the RNI (7.8mg). However, median intake (7mg) was below the RNI. The younger age group (6–9 months) had

Table 9.36 Average daily iron intake (mg) by age and sex

| | Males | | | Females | | | Infants |
	6–9 months	9–12 months	All males	6–9 months	9–12 months	All females	6–12 months
Mean	9.6	7.2	8.6	9.0	6.4	7.7	8.1
Median	9.2	6.0	7.7	8.2	5.7	6.8	7.0
Lower 2.5%	3.3	2.6	3.1	2.8	2.3	2.6	2.7
Upper 2.5%	19.3	17.0	18.5	20.6	15.0	17.7	18.1
SD	4.1	3.7	4.1	4.4	3.3	4.1	4.1
Number of infants	130	96	226	128	134	262	488

Table 9.37 Average daily iron intake (mg) from main food types by age and sex

| | Infants 6–9 months | | Infants 9–12 months | | Total sample | |
	amount	%	amount	%	amount	%
Cereal products of which	0.83	9	1.61	24	1.20	15
—bread	0.20	2	0.41	6	0.30	4
—breakfast cereals	0.50	5	0.90	13	0.69	9
Milk and milk products	0.15	2	0.29	4	0.21	3
Eggs and egg dishes	0.14	2	0.25	4	0.19	2
Fat spreads	0.00	0	0.01	0	0.01	0
Meat and meat products of which	0.26	3	0.46	7	0.36	4
—beef, pork, lamb dishes and products	0.19	2	0.35	5	0.27	3
—offal dishes and products	0.04	0	0.08	1	0.06	1
Fish and fish products	0.02	0	0.05	1	0.03	0
Vegetables	0.17	2	0.41	6	0.29	4
Fruits and nuts	0.05	1	0.06	1	0.05	1
Preserves and confectionery	0.03	0	0.08	1	0.05	1
Beverages	0.02	0	0.05	1	0.03	0
Miscellaneous foods	0.08	1	0.13	2	0.10	1
Commercial infant foods of which	5.49	59	2.68	40	4.15	51
—foods in jars/cans	1.29	14	0.85	13	1.08	13
—instant/dried foods	2.44	26	0.80	12	1.67	21
—rusks	1.72	18	0.99	15	1.37	17
Infant formulas	2.03	22	0.66	10	1.38	17
Breast milk	0.05	1	0.01	0	0.03	0
Total	**9.3**	**100**	**6.7**	**100**	**8.1**	**100**
Number of cases	258		230		488	

significantly greater (p<0.01) intakes than those aged 9–12 months. Iron intake in the older infants was only approximately 70% of the intake of the younger ones (Table 9.36).

The average intake of iron for infants aged 6–9 months was 9.3mg (median 8.8mg) largely as a result of high intakes of fortified infant formulas and commercial infant food. Infants aged 9–12 months had mean intakes of 6.7mg (median 5.8mg) corresponding to 86% (median 74%) of the RNI for infants aged 10–12 months. Almost three quarters of the older infants (73%) had intakes below the RNI, with 21% below the LRNI.

Commercial infant foods including infant formulas provided over 80% (81%) of total iron intake in the younger infants. Although infants aged 9–12 months obtained a large proportion of iron from 'family foods', commercial infant foods and infant formulas continued to be important, providing 50% of their intake (Table 9.37).

Infants from Scotland and Northern England consumed more commercial infant food and infant formulas and had significantly greater (p<0.05) iron intakes (8.5mg; median 7.7mg) than those from the SE, E Anglia and London region (7.5mg, median 6.8mg).

Among infants from both age groups iron intake for those fed solely commercial infant food were significantly greater (p<0.01) compared with those fed predominantly 'family foods' (see Chapter 13 for more details).

Infants whose main type of milk was cows milk, breast milk or low fat milks had significantly (p<0.01) lower iron intakes than those fed infant formulas (see Chapter 16 for more details).

Iron intakes were similar whether other children were present in the family or not. There was also no significant difference in intakes by socioeconomic groups.

Zinc

The average daily intake of zinc for infants aged 6–12 months was 4.5mg (median 4.4mg), which is below the RNI (5mg). Average intakes of zinc were significantly greater (p<0.01) among older infants (4.8mg, median 4.6mg) compared with infants aged 6–9 months (4.3mg, median 4.3mg). Intakes tended to be higher in males than females although this difference was only significant (p<0.05) in the younger infants (males 4.5mg, median 4.5mg; females 4.2mg, median 4.0mg). Seventy-one per cent of all the infants had intakes below the RNI with six per cent below the LRNI.

Among infants aged 6–12 months almost one third (32%) of the total intake was provided by cows milk and milk products. Other important sources were commercial infant food (16%), infant formulas (15%), cereal products (13%) and meat and meat dishes (10%) (Table 9.38).

Table 9.38 Contribution of main food types to average daily intake of zinc (mg) by age

	Infants 6–9 months		Infants 9–12 months		Total sample	
	amount	%	amount	%	amount	%
Cereal products	0.44	10	0.79	17	0.60	13
of which						
—pasta and rice	0.02	0	0.04	1	0.03	1
—breakfast cereals	0.22	5	0.37	8	0.29	6
—bread	0.11	3	0.22	5	0.16	4
—biscuits	0.02	1	0.04	1	0.03	1
—cakes, buns and puddings	0.07	2	0.12	3	0.09	2
Milk and milk products	1.04	24	1.92	40	1.45	32
of which						
—yogurt	0.09	2	0.18	4	0.13	3
Egg and egg dishes	0.09	2	0.16	3	0.13	3
Fat spreads	0.00	0	0.01	0	0.00	0
Meat and meat products	0.36	8	0.58	12	0.46	10
of which						
—beef, pork, lamb dishes and products	0.30	7	0.50	10	0.39	9
—poultry dishes and products	0.02	0	0.04	1	0.03	1
—offal dishes and products	0.04	1	0.04	1	0.04	1
Fish and fish products	0.02	0	0.04	1	0.03	1
Vegetables	0.10	2	0.22	5	0.15	3
Fruits and nuts	0.00	0	0.03	1	0.02	1
Confectionery and preserves	0.00	0	0.00	0	0.00	0
Beverages	0.03	1	0.08	2	0.05	1
Miscellaneous foods	0.04	1	0.06	1	0.05	1
Commercial infant foods	0.97	22	0.49	10	0.75	16
of which						
—foods in jars/cans	0.45	10	0.30	6	0.38	8
—instant/dried foods	0.45	10	0.15	3	0.31	7
—rusks	0.07	2	0.04	1	0.06	1
Infant formulas	1.03	24	0.33	7	0.70	15
Breast milk	0.22	5	0.06	1	0.14	3
Total	**4.3**	**100**	**4.8**	**100**	**4.5**	**100**
Number of cases	258		230		488	

10 | Contribution of milks to the nutrient content of the diet

Milks, including infant formulas, breast milk and cows milk, continued to be an important source of nutrients and energy, providing at least half of the total intake of fat (56%), calcium (59%), riboflavin (61%), phosphorus (50%) and iodine (70%) in the diets of infants aged 6–12 months. Milks also contributed 42% of total energy and 45% of protein. Cows milk is a poor source of iron and vitamins C and D in comparison to infant formulas which are fortified.

Table 10.1 shows the contribution of different milks to selected nutrient intakes in infants from both age groups.

Further information on the reported usage of different types of milk is discussed in Chapter 16.

Table 10.1   Contribution of milks to nutrient intake of infants aged 6–12 months

Infants aged 6–9 months

Nutrient	Unit	Breast milk Amount	%	Infant formulas Amount	%	Cows milk Amount	%	Total milks Amount	%
Energy	kcal	50	6	188	23	146	18	384	47
Protein	g	1.0	3	4.9	18	7.2	26	13.1	47
Fat	g	3.0	9	9.5	29	8.3	25	20.8	63
Carbohydrate	g	5.0	5	22.1	20	11.2	10	38.3	35
Calcium	mg	25	3	155	21	254	34	434	58
Phosphorus	mg	11	2	119	18	205	31	335	51
Iron	mg	0.05	1	2.03	22	0.13	1	2.21	24
Zinc	mg	0.2	5	1.0	24	0.9	21	2.1	50
Iodine	µg	5	3	38	22	82	46	125	71
Riboflavin	mg	0.02	1	0.60	38	0.38	24	1.00	63
Vitamin C	mg	3	2	24	20	3	3	30	25

Infants aged 9–12 months

Nutrient	Unit	Breast milk Amount	%	Infant formulas Amount	%	Cows milk Amount	%	Total milks Amount	%
Energy	kcal	13	1	62	7	261	28	336	36
Protein	g	0.2	1	1.6	5	12.9	37	14.7	43
Fat	g	0.8	2	3.2	8	14.7	38	18.7	48
Carbohydrate	g	1.3	1	7.2	6	20.6	17	29.1	24
Calcium	mg	6	1	49	6	457	55	512	62
Phosphorus	mg	3	0	37	5	370	45	410	50
Iron	mg	0.01	0	0.66	10	0.25	4	0.92	14
Zinc	mg	0.1	1	0.3	7	1.6	34	2.0	42
Iodine	µg	1	1	12	5	146	62	159	68
Riboflavin	mg	0.01	0	0.20	13	0.68	44	0.89	57
Vitamin C	mg	1	1	7	9	6	7	14	17

Table 10.1   Contribution of milks to nutrient intake of infants aged 6–12 months—*continued*

Infants aged 6–12 months

Nutrient	Unit	Breast milk		Infant formulas		Cows milk		Total milks	
		Amount	%	Amount	%	Amount	%	Amount	%
Energy	kcal	32	4	129	15	200	23	361	42
Protein	g	0.6	2	3.0	11	9.9	32	13.5	45
Fat	g	2.0	6	6.5	18	11.4	32	19.9	56
Carbohydrate	g	3.3	3	15.0	13	15.6	14	33.9	30
Calcium	mg	16	2	105	13	349	45	470	59
Phosphorus	mg	7	1	80	11	283	38	370	50
Iron	mg	0.03	0	1.38	17	0.19	2	1.60	19
Zinc	mg	0.1	4	0.7	15	1.1	25	2.0	44
Iodine	µg	3	2	26	13	112	55	141	70
Riboflavin	mg	0.01	1	0.41	26	0.52	34	0.94	61
Vitamin C	mg	2	2	16	16	4	4	22	22

11 Variation in food and nutrient intakes between socioeconomic groups

After preliminary analyses infants were divided by age, since dietary patterns appeared to vary between the younger infants and those aged 9–12 months. Infants from each age group were further divided into socioeconomic groups according to the occupation of the head of household. However, within each of these subgroups there could still be some variation by, for example, sex composition and family size which may also influence dietary patterns in addition to socioeconomic group. The result should therefore be treated with caution and the relationship between dietary patterns and socioeconomic group (or indeed age etc) may not be causal since many other factors may be involved.

Infants aged 6–9 months

Infants aged 6–9 months, irrespective of socioeconomic group, obtained on average a similar proportion of their total energy from most food groups with the exception of milks (Table 11.1). Breast milk provided twice as much energy for infants from the ABC1 socioeconomic group compared with those from the C2DE socio-economic group (80kcal (0.33MJ) and 33kcal (0.14MJ) respectively). This difference was only partially offset by the greater contribution made by infant formulas among those from the C2DE socioeconomic group (ABC1 165kcal (0.69MJ); C2DE 201kcal (0.84MJ)).

Excluding milks, infants, irrespective of socioeconomic group, ate similar types of foods, but those from the C2DE socioeconomic group tended to consume slightly larger quantities of them. These results differ from those obtained in Newcastle upon Tyne during 1968–71, where infants aged 8 months from the 'manual group' derived the extra energy almost entirely from infant formula (Black et al., 1976).

The average daily nutrient intake for infants aged 6–9 months by socioeconomic group is shown in Table 11.2.

The average iron intakes were similar for both socioeconomic groups and exceeded the RNI for infants aged 7–9 months for both socioeconomic groups. Higher iron intakes were reported among non-manual infants aged 8 months from Newcastle upon Tyne during 1968–71 (Black et al., 1976).

The average zinc intake of infants from both socioeconomic groups was similar. Over 70% from each socioeconomic group had intakes below the RNI (ABC1 74%; C2DE 78%) with 8% from both groups below the LRNI.

Table 11.1 Average daily energy (kcal) from main food types by age and socioeconomic group

	Infants aged 6–9 months				Infants aged 9–12 months			
	ABC1		C2DE		ABC1		C2DE	
	amount	%	amount	%	amount	%	amount	%
Cereal and cereal products	89	11	103	13	193	22	201	21
of which								
—bread	21	3	20	2	49	6	44	5
—biscuits and crispbreads	13	2	15	2	27	3	34	4
—cakes, buns and puddings	17	2	21	3	41	5	42	4
Milk and milk products	157	20	171	21	318	36	299	31
of which								
—yogurt	15	2	12	1	32	4	23	2
—cheese and cheese dishes	8	1	5	1	22	2	11	1
Egg and egg dishes	14	2	14	2	24	3	27	3
Fat spreads	10	1	11	1	27	3	25	3
Meat and meat products*	26	3	24	3	46	5	47	5
of which								
—meat, meat products and dishes	19	2	20	2	38	4	41	4
Fish and fish products	5	1	4	1	12	1	8	1
Vegetables	16	2	21	3	39	4	52	5
of which								
—vegetables	6	1	7	1	13	1	14	1
—potatoes	11	1	13	2	22	2	30	3
Fruits and nuts	21	3	14	2	25	3	16	2
Confectionery and preserves	9	1	10	1	14	2	24	2
Beverages	9	1	16	2	27	3	51	5
of which								
—fruit juice	3	0	3	0	6	1	7	1
—soft drinks	4	1	4	0	13	1	17	2
Miscellaneous foods	5	1	10	1	7	1	16	2
Commercial infant foods	194	24	190	23	101	11	97	10
of which								
—foods in jars/cans	60	7	71	9	38	4	45	5
—instant/dried foods	89	11	70	9	30	3	25	3
—rusks	23	3	29	4	13	1	16	2
—fruit juices and drinks	22	3	20	2	20	2	12	1
Infant formulas	165	21	201	24	29	3	77	8
Breast milk	80	10	33	4	19	2	10	1
Total	**802**	**100**	**822**	**100**	**881**	**100**	**949**	**100**
Number of cases	91		167		72		158	

*Includes meat, poultry, offal, meat products and dishes.

Infants aged 9–12 months

The average daily nutrient intake for infants aged 9–12 months by socioeconomic group is shown in Table 11.3.

Among the older infants, groups of food generally provided a similar proportion of total energy intake in both socioeconomic groups. However, intakes of infant formulas and milk and milk products did vary considerably between the two groups. Infant formulas provided 8% of total energy in those from the C2DE socioeconomic group but only 3% in those from ABC1 socio-economic group, whereas cows milk and milk products such as yoghurt and cheese were more popular in the ABC1 socioeconomic

Table 11.2 Average daily nutrient intake for infants aged 6–9 months by socioeconomic group

Nutrient	Unit	ABC1 (n=91)			C2DE (n=167)		
		Mean	Median	SD	Mean	Median	SD
Energy	kcal	802	781	173	822	795	194
	MJ	3.37	3.29	0.73	3.46	3.34	0.82
Protein	g	26.7	25.9	8.1	27.8	26.3	8.3
Fat	g	32.2	31.6	8.3	33.3	31.9	9.0
Starch	g	36.8	37.3	13.9	37.7	35.0	15.9
Total sugars	g	71.3	66.4	21.3	72.0	69.3	20.3
Carbohydrate	g	108.1	104.9	26.3	109.7	106.7	28.6
Dietary fibre	g	3.7	3.5	1.7	3.6	3.3	1.7
Sodium	mg	545	477	261	613	563	281
Potassium	mg	1222	1199	335	1248	1221	336
Calcium	mg	721	712	236	757	732	249
Magnesium	mg	109	108	36	112	107	35
Phosphorus	mg	642	634	219	683	669	224
Iron	mg	9.1	8.4	4.3	9.4	8.9	4.2
Copper	mg	0.6	0.5	0.2	0.6	0.5	0.2
Zinc	mg	4.3	4.3	1.0	4.4	4.3	1.1
Chloride	mg	901	792	991	393	907	426
Iodine	μg	166	158	72	182	173	75
Manganese	mg	1.1	1.0	0.5	1.1	1.0	0.5
Retinol	μg	601	450	374	617	526	389
Carotene	μg	1011	736	820	1037	802	773
Retinol equivalent	μg	769	623	393	790	724	401
Vitamin D	μg	4.2	1.5	4.9	5.0	3.4	4.7
Vitamin E	mg	4.2	3.1	2.3	4.6	4.1	2.5
Thiamin	mg	1.1	1.1	0.4	1.2	1.2	0.4
Riboflavin	mg	1.5	1.5	0.7	1.6	1.6	0.6
Niacin	mg	6.1	5.2	3.1	6.2	5.8	2.9
Niacin equivalent	mg	12.4	12.1	3.6	12.5	12.4	3.5
Vitamin C	mg	117	93	81	117	103	83
Vitamin B_6	mg	0.8	0.8	0.3	0.8	0.8	0.3
Vitamin B_{12}	μg	2.8	2.7	0.2	3.1	3.0	0.2
Folate	μg	104	104	26	105	100	27
Pantothenic acid	mg	3.9	3.8	1.3	4.0	3.7	1.1
Biotin	μg	24.0	20.7	19.5	28.0	23.1	27.6
Saturated fatty acids	g	15.4	15.1	4.5	16.2	15.9	5.0
Monounsaturated fatty acids	g	9.8	9.7	2.8	9.8	9.7	2.8
Polyunsaturated fatty acids	g	3.3	2.8	1.5	3.2	2.8	1.5
Cholesterol	mg	144	140	56	152	144	58
Glucose	g	7.6	6.6	4.9	6.7	5.5	4.8
Fructose	g	7.0	5.9	5.2	5.9	4.8	4.3
Sucrose	g	14.0	12.4	8.3	15.9	14.9	8.1
Maltose	g	1.5	0.9	2.0	1.7	0.9	2.5
Lactose	g	38.5	35.5	17.5	38.2	36.4	17.6
Others/dextrins	g	2.8	1.5	3.5	3.6	1.7	4.1

group (36%; C2DE 31% of total energy respectively). On average infants from the C2DE socioeconomic group had higher energy intakes, obtaining more energy from infant formulas, vegetables including potatoes, confectionery, beverages such as squashes, carbonates and sweetened hot drinks and miscellaneous foods but less from breast milk and fruit compared with those from the ABC1 socioeconomic group.

On average, iron intakes tended to be greater among infants from the C2DE socioeconomic group although this difference was not significant. Infants aged 9–12 months from both socioeconomic groups obtained approximately 40% of their total iron intake from

Table 11.3 Average daily nutrient intake for infants aged 9–12 months by socioeconomic group

Nutrient	Unit	ABC1 (n=72)			C2DE (n=158)		
		Mean	Median	SD	Mean	Median	SD
Energy	kcal	881	867	138	949	915	245
	MJ	3.71	3.66	0.58	3.99	3.85	1.03
Protein	g	34.0	33.7	7.4	34.7	33.8	9.9
Fat	g	36.2	36.4	7.7	39.6	39.1	13.0
Starch	g	44.4	42.7	12.1	47.6	46.1	16.4
Total sugars	g	67.4	68.6	13.8	73.5	71.2	20.5
Carbohydrate	g	111.8	113.6	19.8	121.0	116.0	31.3
Dietary fibre	g	5.0	4.7	1.9	4.7	4.4	1.8
Sodium	mg	878	872	237	973	903	376
Potassium	mg	1442	1445	321	1496	1434	403
Calcium	mg	812	806	245	831	811	282
Magnesium	mg	138	136	32	141	136	40
Phosphorus	mg	819	829	209	827	810	247
Iron	mg	6.2	5.9	2.7	7.0	5.8	3.8
Copper	mg	0.6	0.5	0.3	0.6	0.6	0.2
Zinc	mg	4.7	4.7	0.9	4.8	4.5	1.3
Chloride	mg	1382	1380	361	1524	1427	569
Iodine	µg	228	238	76	238	233	89
Manganese	mg	1.2	1.2	0.5	1.2	1.2	0.5
Retinol	µg	566	364	645	538	395	422
Carotene	µg	1236	1003	919	1170	886	857
Retinol equivalent	µg	772	614	668	733	617	451
Vitamin D	µg	1.6	0.9	2.1	2.4	1.0	3.7
Vitamin E	mg	3.2	2.7	1.7	3.7	3.0	2.1
Thiamin	mg	0.9	0.9	0.3	1.1	1.0	0.4
Riboflavin	mg	1.4	1.4	0.4	1.6	1.5	0.6
Niacin	mg	4.2	3.6	1.9	4.9	4.3	2.5
Niacin equivalent	mg	11.9	11.8	2.5	12.8	12.1	3.7
Vitamin C	mg	89	64	75	78	55	72
Vitamin B_6	mg	0.8	0.8	0.2	0.9	0.8	0.3
Vitamin B_{12}	µg	3.5	3.4	1.4	3.3	3.1	1.2
Folate	µg	104	105	25	108	101	31
Pantothenic acid	mg	3.3	3.3	0.9	3.6	3.2	1.3
Biotin	µg	25.0	21.0	27.4	23.1	21.6	10.7
Saturated fatty acids	g	18.3	18.6	4.8	20.1	19.9	7.1
Monounsaturated fatty acids	g	11.3	11.1	2.3	12.2	11.8	4.4
Polyunsaturated fatty acids	g	3.7	3.6	1.3	3.8	3.5	1.6
Cholesterol	mg	177	160	80	187	173	77
Glucose	g	8.9	7.3	5.6	7.2	6.1	4.7
Fructose	g	7.6	6.6	4.2	6.4	5.2	4.7
Sucrose	g	19.9	19.3	8.5	23.2	21.3	10.4
Maltose	g	1.4	0.7	2.4	1.3	0.8	1.6
Lactose	g	28.2	27.7	10.5	33.6	30.7	16.9
Others/dextrins	g	1.4	1.1	2.1	1.7	1.0	2.2

commercial infant foods whereas infant formulas provided 12% and 5% for those from the C2DE and ABC1 socioeconomic groups respectively. Average iron intake was 79% of the RNI for infants from the ABC1 socioeconomic group and 90% for those from the C2DE socioeconomic group with just over a quarter (26%) and 19% respectively with intakes below the LRNI.

Although zinc intakes were on average greater in the older age group, 63% of infants from the ABC1 socioeconomic group and 66% from the C2DE socioeconomic group were still below the RNI with 3% and 5% respectively below the LRNI.

12 Variation in food and nutrient intakes for infants with and without siblings

The presence of other children may affect the type of foods available in a household and the past experiences of the mother may influence the choices of food for her infant. Thus the food and nutrient intake of first and subsequent children may differ. To explore this possibility infants from each age group were further subdivided according to whether other children were present in the family or not.

Infants aged 6–9 months

The average daily nutrient intake for infants aged 6–9 months with and without siblings is shown in Table 12.1.

Infants who were the only child in the family had greater intakes of most nutrients (except sodium, chloride, manganese and sucrose) compared with those who had siblings, and the differences were significant for vitamin C ($p<0.01$), thiamin ($p<0.025$), copper ($p<0.05$), niacin equivalent ($p<0.05$), glucose ($p<0.025$), and fructose ($p<0.05$). These higher intakes were largely a result of a greater consumption of commercial infant food by infants with no siblings.

In both groups average intakes of all nutrients besides zinc and vitamin D met or were above the RNI. Amongst infants who were the only child in the family 73% had average zinc intakes below the RNI (6% below the LRNI) compared with 78% (9% below the LRNI) who had siblings.

Infants who were the only child in the family had an average vitamin D intake of 4.9μg (median 4.0μg; mean 71% of the RNI) compared with 4.6μg (median 1.7μg; mean 65% of the RNI) for those who had siblings.

Infants aged 9–12 months

The average daily nutrient intake for infants aged 9–12 months with and without siblings is shown in Table 12.2.

Infants with siblings had significantly greater intakes of fat ($p<0.05$), sucrose ($p<0.025$), sodium ($p<0.05$), chloride ($p<0.05$), monounsaturated fatty acids ($p<0.025$) and polyunsaturated fatty acids ($p<0.01$) compared with those who were the only child in the family. These differences were largely due to greater consumption of 'family foods'. However vitamin C intakes were significantly greater ($p<0.05$) for those with no siblings and this was due to a greater consumption of commercial infant food, many of which are fortified.

Table 12.1 Average daily nutrient intake for infants aged 6–9 months with and without siblings

Nutrient	Units	Only child (89)			With siblings (169)		
		Mean	Median	SD	Mean	Median	SD
Energy	kcal	835	823	162	805	777	199
	MJ	3.51	3.47	0.68	3.39	3.28	0.84
Protein	g	28.1	27.8	8.3	27.1	25.9	8.2
Fat	g	33.7	32.9	7.4	32.5	31.5	9.4
Carbohydrate	g	111.7	106.9	24.8	107.8	104.5	29.2
Starch	g	38.2	35.7	16.1	36.9	36.0	14.7
Total sugars	g	73.5	71.5	17.9	70.9	66.4	21.9
Dietary fibre	g	3.6	3.3	1.7	3.6	3.5	1.7
Sodium	mg	586	524	264	590	556	283
Potassium	mg	1267	1233	332	1224	1210	337
Calcium	mg	771	745	257	730	715	238
Magnesium	mg	112	101	35	110	110	36
Phosphorus	mg	691	649	224	657	651	221
Iron	mg	9.7	9.2	3.7	9.1	8.1	4.5
Copper	mg	0.6	0.6	0.2	0.6	0.5	0.2
Zinc	mg	4.5	4.4	1.0	4.3	4.2	1.1
Chloride	mg	952	864	401	963	874	425
Manganese	mg	1.1	1.0	0.4	1.1	1.0	0.5
Iodine	µg	179	164	78	175	164	72
Retinol	µg	648	597	383	592	481	383
Carotene	µg	1046	826	779	1018	746	796
Retinol equivalent	µg	822	759	395	762	677	398
Vitamin D	µg	4.9	4.0	4.3	4.6	1.7	5.0
Vitamin E	mg	4.6	4.3	2.2	4.4	3.3	2.6
Thiamin	mg	1.2	1.2	0.3	1.1	1.1	0.4
Riboflavin	mg	1.6	1.6	0.5	1.5	1.5	0.7
Niacin	mg	6.5	6.4	2.7	6.0	5.2	3.1
Niacin equivalent	mg	12.9	12.5	3.1	12.2	12.0	3.7
Vitamin B_6	mg	0.8	0.9	0.2	0.8	0.8	0.3
Vitamin B_{12}	µg	3.1	3.1	1.1	2.9	2.9	1.2
Folate	µg	107	107	23	103	98	29
Pantothenic acid	mg	4.1	4.1	1.2	3.9	3.5	1.4
Biotin	µg	27.5	23.3	28.3	26.0	21.2	23.3
Vitamin C	mg	140	121	87	105	90	77
Saturated fatty acids	g	16.4	15.3	4.7	15.6	15.7	4.9
Monounsaturated fatty acids	g	9.9	9.9	2.5	9.7	9.7	3.0
Polyunsaturated fatty acids	g	3.3	3.0	1.3	3.2	2.7	1.5
Cholesterol	mg	151	150	57	147	139	58
Glucose	g	8.0	6.9	5.4	6.5	5.7	4.5
Fructose	g	7.0	5.4	5.5	5.9	5.2	4.2
Sucrose	g	14.7	12.2	7.7	15.6	14.5	8.5
Maltose	g	1.8	1.2	2.7	1.5	0.9	2.1
Lactose	g	38.7	38.2	14.7	38.1	34	18.9
Dextrins/other	g	3.3	1.8	3.5	3.3	1.5	4.1

In both groups, average intakes of all nutrients besides iron, zinc and vitamin D were above the RNIs. Iron intakes were on average 7.2mg (median 6.1mg; mean 92% of the RNI) for infants with no siblings and 6.5mg (median 5.8mg; mean 84% of the RNI) for those with siblings; 17% and 23% of infants respectively had intakes below the LRNI. Three per cent of infants with no siblings and 5% with siblings had average zinc intakes below the LRNI. Both groups had on average vitamin D intakes which were half the RNI (7µg).

Table 12.2 Average daily nutrient intake for infants aged 9–12 months with and without siblings

Nutrient	Units	Only child (75) Mean	Median	SD	With siblings (155) Mean	Median	SD
Energy	kcal	903	880	204	940	905	225
	MJ	3.8	3.7	0.86	3.95	3.81	0.95
Protein	g	34.2	33.6	8.9	34.6	33.9	9.3
Fat	g	36.8	36.1	11.0	39.5	38.2	12.0
Carbohydrate	g	116.0	114.7	29.7	119.2	115.0	28.0
Starch	g	44.9	44.2	16.3	47.3	46.3	14.6
Total sugars	g	71.1	71.0	18.9	71.8	69.6	18.9
Dietary fibre	g	4.7	4.7	1.7	4.8	4.5	1.9
Sodium	mg	882	863	325	972	917	346
Potassium	mg	1456	1461	352	1490	1426	392
Calcium	mg	829	812	259	823	806	276
Magnesium	mg	139	138	35	140	136	39
Phosphorus	mg	830	836	220	822	812	244
Iron	mg	7.2	6.1	3.8	6.5	5.8	3.3
Copper	mg	0.6	0.6	0.2	0.6	0.5	0.2
Zinc	mg	4.9	4.7	1.2	4.7	4.5	1.2
Chloride	mg	1394	1351	504	1521	1441	519
Manganese	mg	1.2	1.2	0.5	1.2	1.2	0.5
Iodine	µg	232	236	84	236	237	86
Retinol	µg	552	464	346	544	361	563
Carotene	µg	1190	1028	816	1191	877	906
Retinol equivalent	µg	751	671	376	742	568	588
Vitamin D	µg	2.3	1.1	3.1	2.1	0.9	3.4
Vitamin E	mg	3.5	2.8	1.9	3.5	3.0	2.1
Thiamin	mg	1.0	1.0	0.4	1.0	0.9	0.4
Riboflavin	mg	1.5	1.5	0.5	1.5	1.4	0.5
Niacin	mg	4.7	4.1	2.5	4.7	4.1	2.3
Niacin equivalent	mg	12.5	11.9	3.6	12.5	12.1	3.3
Vitamin B_6	mg	0.8	0.8	0.2	0.8	0.8	0.3
Vitamin B_{12}	µg	3.4	3.3	1.1	3.4	3.1	1.4
Folate	µg	105	100	26	108	103	31
Pantothenic acid	mg	3.5	3.4	1.1	3.5	3.2	1.2
Biotin	µg	22.6	21.9	6.7	24.4	20.9	21.0
Vitamin C	mg	95	72	81	75	54	69
Saturated fatty acids	g	18.7	18.1	6.2	19.9	19.8	6.6
Monounsaturated fatty acids	g	11.2	11.1	3.4	12.3	11.9	3.7
Polyunsaturated fatty acids	g	3.5	3.3	1.3	4.0	3.6	1.6
Cholesterol	mg	185	164	86	183	172	74
Glucose	g	8.0	6.5	5.1	7.6	6.4	5.0
Fructose	g	7.1	5.8	5.0	6.7	5.6	4.4
Sucrose	g	20.1	18.0	9.3	23.2	21.0	10.1
Maltose	g	1.2	0.8	1.2	1.5	0.7	2.1
Lactose	g	33.0	30.2	14.2	31.4	28.7	15.9
Dextrins/other	g	1.9	1.2	2.2	1.5	0.9	2.2

Variation in food intake

The feeding patterns in families where the infant was the only child differed from those where other children were present (see Tables 12.3 and 12.4).

Infants aged 6–9 months

Commercial infant foods were more important as a source of energy in the diets of infants who were the only child in the family, providing 26% (219kcal (0.92MJ)) of the total energy compared with 22% (177kcal (0.74MJ)) for those infants with siblings, whereas 'family foods' contributed 27% (224kcal (0.94MJ)) and 31% (249kcal (1.04MJ)) respectively.

Table 12.3 Consumption of food groups by consumers aged 6–9 months with and without siblings (g/infant/week)

Food group	No sibling			With sibling		
	Mean	Median	% who ate	Mean	Median	% who ate
Pasta and rice	104	90	19	135	96	28
Breakfast cereals	165	85	61	157	130	69
Bread	96	62	58	91	71	69
Biscuits and crispbread	48	28	46	40	25	51
Cakes, buns and puddings	216	125	47	184	130	54
Milk	2279	2082	67	2026	1594	77
Cream	32	21	9	38	28	14
Yogurt	240	128	33	292	241	39
Cheese and cheese dishes	71	34	28	59	28	38
Eggs and egg dishes	83	57	54	90	64	56
Fat spreads	20	15	54	18	11	59
Meat products and dishes	212	135	58	155	100	62
Offal and offal dishes	79	45	9	69	22	8
Poultry and poultry dishes	67	26	38	92	40	28
Fish products	61	53	25	71	45	40
Vegetables excluding potatoes	148	85	64	147	118	67
Potatoes	140	108	64	166	125	73
Fruit	189	140	55	208	140	73
Nuts and nut spreads	16	19	3	21	21	2
Preserves	23	18	19	39	13	18
Chocolate confectionery	24	13	31	31	22	36
Sugar confectionery	16	16	1	16	16	1
Crisps and savoury snacks	17	14	4	12	7	8
Fruit juice	317	184	19	212	138	23
Tea and coffee	684	311	26	728	455	27
Squash and soft drinks	419	105	17	609	314	24
Powdered drinks, dry weight	36	23	3	—	—	0
Miscellaneous foods	175	100	57	200	116	69
Infant foods						
Foods in jars and cans	1120	928	78	993	777	72
Instant food, dried	202	151	75	188	150	67
Rusks	73	49	58	82	55	59
Infant formulas	3202	3389	58	3736	3473	49
Fruit juices and drinks	804	502	81	653	407	60
Breast milk	3083	3341	13	2533	2107	22

Quantity of squashes, fruit juices are as consumed, i.e. where necessary a dilution factor has been applied.

Infants aged 9–12 months

'Family foods' provided 56% of the total energy (523kcal (2.19MJ)) for infants with siblings compared with 48% (434kcal (1.82MJ)) for those who were the only child in the family. Conversely commercial infant foods contributed 9% (87kcal (0.36MJ)) and 14% (123kcal (0.51MJ)) of the total energy in the diets of infants with and without siblings respectively.

Table 12.4 Consumption of food groups by consumers aged 9–12 months with and without siblings (g/infant/week)

Food group	No sibling			With sibling		
	Mean	Median	% who ate	Mean	Median	% who ate
Pasta and rice	145	126	51	144	90	54
Breakfast cereals	186	140	92	214	140	90
Bread	123	106	91	147	126	97
Biscuits and crispbread	52	41	77	59	48	90
Cakes, buns and puddings	248	212	67	227	180	81
Milk	2882	2924	95	2916	2998	97
Cream	57	50	12	60	34	28
Yogurt	418	337	55	347	300	58
Cheese and cheese dishes	64	30	53	68	48	57
Eggs and egg dishes	127	100	64	131	108	72
Fat spreads	25	22	79	30	26	95
Meat products and dishes	218	223	83	196	162	90
Offal and offal dishes	47	27	19	90	60	12
Poultry and poultry dishes	95	40	35	57	40	47
Fish products	83	56	52	66	56	57
Vegetables excluding potatoes	176	147	83	230	186	94
Potatoes	215	186	80	248	200	95
Fruit	251	192	68	196	170	79
Nuts and nut spreads	15	16	5	20	15	6
Preserves	27	18	33	33	27	38
Chocolate confectionery	32	25	55	40	31	57
Sugar confectionery	32	18	12	26	13	10
Crisps and savoury snacks	26	14	21	32	22	39
Fruit juice	309	197	35	361	149	40
Tea and coffee	757	729	32	1347	822	51
Squash and soft drinks	816	360	33	886	695	54
Powdered drinks, dry weight	17	17	3	42	42	1
Miscellaneous foods	207	120	80	240	169	89
Infant foods						
Foods in jars and cans	1079	845	53	866	670	50
Instant food, dried	171	120	33	160	93	26
Rusks	50	29	55	72	50	35
Infant formulas	2427	1709	27	3312	3472	17
Fruit juices and drinks	834	448	61	792	352	35
Breast milk	1282	700	13	1338	1400	8

Quantity of squashes, fruit juices are as consumed, i.e. where necessary a dilution factor has been applied.

Food and nutrient intakes of infants fed predominantly commercial infant foods, 'family foods' or both

Infants were divided into three groups according to whether the mother reported that, with the exception of the type of milk used, they consumed only commercial infant food, 'family foods' or both (questions 17 and 18 of the questionnaire, see Appendix III). These groups have been further subdivided by age.

Table 13.1 Numbers of infants in each age group reported to be consuming a diet consisting of predominant food types

| | 6–9 months | | 9–12 months | |
	Number	%	Number	%
Commercial infant food only	31	12	6	3
'Family food' only	19	7	71	31
Commercial infant food and 'family foods'	208	81	153	67
Total	**258**	**100**	**230**	**100**

Although 90 mothers reported that their infants were non-consumers of commercial infant food, during the recording week 13 of these infants did consume small amounts of commercial infant food.

Selected nutrient intakes are shown in Table 13.2. The majority of infants were fed a wide range of both 'family foods' and commercial infant foods. Only a small number in each age group were fed solely on one category of food and therefore caution is required when interpreting these results.

Infants aged 6–9 months

Infants reported to be fed solely commercial infant foods had significantly greater intakes of total sugars ($p<0.01$), iron ($p<0.01$), vitamin D ($p<0.01$) and vitamin C ($p<0.01$) than those receiving solely 'family foods'. However, protein and dietary fibre intakes were significantly greater ($p<0.01$) for those fed predominantly 'family foods'.

Energy intakes were considerably lower for those infants reported to be fed solely on commercial infant food (740kcal) but the difference was only significant ($p<0.01$) when compared with those fed both 'family' and commercial infant foods (826kcal). Among infants reported to be fed only 'family foods' fat provided a greater proportion of their total energy (38%) compared with those receiving only commercial infant foods (37%) or both (36%). Sugars provided 37%

Table 13.2 Average daily intake of selected nutrients for infants fed either predominantly commercial infant foods, 'family foods' or both

		Infants aged 6–9 months						Infants aged 9–12 months					
		Commercial infant food		Both		'Family foods'		Commercial infant food		Both		'Family foods'	
		Mean	SD	Mean	SD	Mean	SD	Mean	SD	Mean	SD	Mean	SD
Energy	kcal	740	140	826	191	817	190	887	125	919	193	950	272
	MJ	3.11	0.59	3.48	0.80	3.44	0.80	3.73	0.52	3.87	0.81	4.00	1.14
Protein	g	22.3	6.1	27.8	8.0	31.7	10.1	32.3	9.2	33.8	8.1	36.0	11.2
Fat	g	30.1	6.9	33.2	8.9	34.6	9.3	36.7	8.0	37.7	10.5	40.6	14.1
Dietary fibre	g	2.3	1.0	3.7	1.7	4.7	1.7	3.4	1.3	4.7	1.8	5.0	2.0
Calcium	mg	725	233	754	248	677	225	999	382	833	247	794	305
Iron	mg	10.1	4.6	9.6	4.1	4.6	1.7	10.5	2.2	7.5	3.6	4.9	2.3
Zinc	mg	3.9	0.7	4.4	1.1	4.5	1.3	4.8	0.9	4.7	1.1	4.8	1.5
Vitamin D	µg	6.1	5.2	4.8	4.8	1.3	1.9	4.3	4.4	2.3	3.2	1.6	3.3
Vitamin C	mg	160	101	117	78	46	27	126	43	89	75	60	67
Sucrose	g	11.5	7.0	15.6	8.2	17.1	8.4	14.0	4.3	21.8	9.5	23.6	10.8
Number of cases		31		208		19		6		153		71	

of total energy intake for infants fed solely on commercial infant foods compared with 27% for those fed predominantly 'family foods'. Protein intake was lower for infants reported to be consuming only commercial infant foods but was still well above the RNI for infants aged 7–9 months. Infants fed solely 'family foods' had significantly lower (p<0.01) iron intakes (4.6mg, median 4.4mg) than those fed either commercial infant foods (10.1mg, median 9.4mg) or both (9.6mg, median 9.2mg) (Table 13.3). The average iron intake of infants who were 'reported to not consume any commercial infant foods' was only 59% of the RNI (Table 13.3). Indeed all 19 infants fed solely 'family foods' had iron intakes below the RNI. The proportion of infants with iron intakes below the LRNI was 37% for those fed solely 'family foods' 10% for commercial infant food and 6% for those fed both types of food.

Average zinc intakes were slightly below the RNI in all three groups. Among the 31 infants reported to be fed only 'commercial infant foods' the average intake was 3.9mg (78% of the RNI). Infants fed solely 'family foods' had an average intake of 4.5mg (90% of the RNI) compared to 4.4mg (88% of the RNI) for infants receiving both types of food. Sixteen per cent of infants fed either solely commercial infant food or 'family foods' had zinc intakes below the LRNI compared to 6% for those fed both food types.

Vitamin D intakes were considerably below the RNI (7µg) in all three groups. Infants reported to be fed only 'family foods' had average intakes of 1.3µg (median 0.8µg; mean 19% of the RNI) compared to 6.1µg (median 5.3µg) for those fed predominantly commercial infant food (86% of the RNI) whereas those fed both types of food were intermediate at 4.8µg (median 2.9µg) vitamin D (mean 69% of the RNI).

Fortification of many commercial infant desserts, infant fruit juices and drinks resulted in consumers of these products having very high intakes of vitamin C. Although infants reported to be fed solely 'family foods' had significantly lower (p<0.01) vitamin C intakes compared with those receiving any commercial infant food, average intakes were well in excess of the RNI.

Infants reported to be fed only commercial infant foods obtained more energy from milks (59%) largely from infant formulas compared with those fed solely 'family foods' (39%), mainly as cows milk. Infant formulas which are fortified with iron provided 2.6mg (26% of the total) for infants fed predominantly commercial infant food whereas all milks (including infant formulas, cows milk and breast milk) provided only 0.6mg (13% of the total) for those infants fed solely 'family foods'. Important sources of iron in the diets of infants fed predominantly 'family foods' were cereal products (39%), largely breakfast cereals, many of which are fortified, commercial infant food (15%) many of which are also fortified, meat and meat products (13%), vegetables (8%) and infant formulas (7%).

Table 13.3 Average daily iron intake (mg) from main food groups by age and reported predominance of the types of foods fed to infants

| | Infants 6–9 months | | | | | | Infants 9–12 months | | | | | |
| | Commercial infant food | | 'Family foods' | | Both | | Commercial infant food | | 'Family foods' | | Both | |
	amount	%	amount	%	amount	%	amount	%	amount	%	amount	%
Cereals	0.19	2	1.78	39	0.84	9	0.96	9	2.00	41	1.47	19
of which												
—bread	0.02	0	0.36	8	0.21	2	0.12	1	0.50	10	0.39	5
—breakfast cereals	0.15	1	1.21	26	0.49	5	0.68	6	1.15	24	0.79	11
Milk and milk products	0.08	1	0.23	5	0.15	1	0.24	2	0.30	6	0.28	4
of which												
—cows milk	0.08	1	0.20	4	0.13	1	0.23	2	0.26	5	0.24	3
Eggs and egg dishes	0.04	0	0.20	4	0.15	1	0.03	0	0.27	5	0.24	3
Fat spreads	0.00	0	0.01	0	0.00	0	0.00	0	0.01	0	0.01	0
Meat and meat products	0.00	0	0.57	13	0.26	2	0.00	0	0.64	13	0.39	5
of which												
—beef, pork, lamb dishes and products	0.00	0	0.50	11	0.19	2	0.00	0	0.49	10	0.30	4
—offal dishes and products	0.00	0	0.03	1	0.04	0	0.00	0	0.11	2	0.07	1
Fish and fish dishes	0.00	0	0.03	1	0.02	0	0.00	0	0.06	1	0.05	1
Vegetables	0.02	0	0.36	8	0.18	2	0.01	0	0.56	12	0.37	5
Fruits and nuts	0.01	0	0.07	2	0.05	1	0.01	0	0.06	1	0.06	1
Preserves and confectionery	0.01	0	0.04	1	0.04	0	0.03	0	0.12	2	0.08	1
Beverages	0.04	0	0.03	1	0.02	0	0.03	0	0.06	1	0.04	1
Miscellaneous foods	0.00	0	0.14	3	0.09	1	0.00	0	0.17	3	0.12	2
Commercial infant food	7.08	70	0.69	15	5.68	59	6.92	66	0.25	5	3.62	49
of which												
—foods in jars/cans	1.98	19	0.14	3	1.29	13	3.22	31	0.03	1	1.14	15
—instant/dried foods	3.46	34	0.40	9	2.47	26	1.90	18	0.02	1	1.13	15
—rusks	1.60	16	0.14	3	1.88	19	1.73	17	0.19	4	1.32	18
Infant formulas	2.60	26	0.34	7	2.10	22	2.25	21	0.41	8	0.72	10
Breast milk	0.07	1	0.08	2	0.05	0	0.00	0	0.01	0	0.02	0
Total	**10.1**	**100**	**4.6**	**100**	**9.6**	**100**	**10.5**	**100**	**4.9**	**100**	**7.5**	**100**
Number of cases	31		19		208		6		71		153	

Although mothers may have reported not feeding any commercial infant food to their infant at the interview, this may not have been the case during the recording week. Therefore there may be some foods which surprisingly provide nutrients in groups of infants who were reported to be fed none of this type of food.

Infants aged 9–12 months

Fewer than 3% of the older infants were reported to be fed solely commercial infant foods and it is therefore difficult to make firm conclusions on such a small sample. However, in common with the younger infants they had significantly greater intakes of iron (p<0.01) and vitamin C (p<0.01) but markedly lower dietary fibre (p<0.01) intakes. Energy intakes tended to be lower and sucrose consumption was significantly lower (p<0.01) for infants fed solely commercial infant foods compared to those fed entirely 'family foods'. In the small group of infants fed solely commercial infant food, energy intakes tended to be lower.

Although zinc intakes were greater amongst the older infants than those aged 6–9 months, on average intakes were still below the RNI for all three groups. Amongst infants fed solely 'family foods' 6% had intakes below the LRNI compared to 4% for those fed both types of food. The main sources of zinc for infants fed predominantly 'family foods' were cows milk (35% of the total intake), meat and meat dishes (14%), breakfast cereals (9%) and bread (5%).

Vitamin C intakes were well in excess of the RNI in all the groups due to the consumption of fortified commercial infant fruit juices and drinks.

Intakes of vitamin D were considerably below the RNI in all the groups. Infants reported to be fed solely 'family foods' had average intakes of 1.6μg (median 0.8μg) compared with 4.3μg (median 3.7μg) for those predominantly fed commercial infant foods.

Cows milk provided a greater proportion of the total energy for the older infants from all groups. Infants reported to be fed solely commercial infant food obtained 54% of their total energy from milks (infant formulas 20%; cows milk 34%) compared with 33% for those fed only 'family food' (infant formulas 4%; cows milk 29%).

Iron intakes showed the same pattern reported for the younger infants. Infants reported to be fed only 'family foods' had significantly lower (p<0.01) iron intake (4.9mg iron, median 4.5mg, 63% of the RNI for infants aged 7–12 months) compared with those fed either predominantly commercial infant food (10.5mg, median 11.3mg, 134% of the RNI) or both food types (7.5mg, median 6.7mg, 96% of the RNI). Forty-two per cent of the older infants fed solely 'family foods' had intakes below the LRNI compared with 12% fed both types. None of the six infants reported to be receiving solely commercial infant food had an average iron intake below the LRNI. One infant (17%) had an average iron intake below the RNI. The main sources of iron for each group were similar to those observed in the younger infants (Table 13.3).

An intake of a nutrient lower than the RNI does not necessarily imply deficiency which can be established only by biochemical or clinical assessment of nutritional status. However, iron deficiency has been recognised as a potential problem of infants and toddlers (Dallman, 1986).

There are two broad categories of iron in food: haem iron which accounts for about 40% of the iron in meat and fish dishes and non-haem iron which is found in cereal products, vegetables and in fortified foods. Haem iron is relatively well absorbed and largely unaffected by other constituents in the diet. The absorption of non-haem iron depends on how soluble it becomes in the intestine. This is determined primarily by the composition of foods that are eaten in the iron containing meal. The absorption of non-haem iron is increased by the presence of vitamin C or by relatively small amounts of meat, fish or poultry in the meal. On the other hand, iron absorption is decreased by factors such as tannins in tea (Fairweather-Tait, 1989). Although meat and meat dishes were consumed by the majority of infants, they were only a minor part of the infants' diet. Less than one sixth of the iron in the diets of infants fed 'family foods' was from meat and fish dishes. Thus the vast majority of the iron was non-haem iron.

Vitamin C intake from food alone was high, providing on average four times the RNI, largely from fortified fruit juices or drinks and desserts. Even for infants fed on 'family foods' intakes were well above the RNI. Thus, although their iron intake was low, the high vitamin C intake may help to protect the infants from deficiency. However, consumption of tea was also common, which would tend to reduce iron absorption. Although infants fed 'family foods' did consume iron fortified foods such as breakfast cereals, the levels of fortification in these foods is much lower than in infant cereals.

The iron status of older infants is an area that warrants further investigation, particularly as the dietary pattern associated with low iron intakes is likely to be followed by increasing numbers in the early pre-school years, when commercial infant foods and infant formulas are completely replaced by cows milk and 'family foods'.

14 Comparison of selected nutrient intakes from food for infants who received vitamin supplements and those who were non-supplement users

Table 14.1 shows the type of foods which provided energy and vitamins A, C and D for infants who received supplements and those who did not.

Intakes of energy and vitamins A and C from food were on average very similar for infants receiving supplements and for those who were not.

Milks made a similar contribution to total energy intakes in both groups, however supplement users derived more energy from cows milk and less from infant formulas whereas for non-supplement users the pattern was reversed. Average intakes of vitamin D from food were 3.77µg (median 1.23µg) for infants not receiving supplements compared with 3.14µg (median 1.15µg) for those who were. This difference, although not significant, may be as a result of the lower consumption of infant formulas amongst supplement users.

Vitamin supplements were given to 43% of infants usually in the quantity recommended by The Panel on Child Nutrition of the Committee on Medical Aspects of Food Policy (DHSS, 1988). A daily dose of 5 drops of children's vitamin drops, available from Child Health Clinics and free to certain mothers through the Welfare Food Scheme, would provide 200µg vitamin A, 20mg vitamin C and 7µg vitamin D. Using this information, together with that obtained from the interview on the frequency and dose given, it was possible to calculate for each infant, the percentage contribution that these supplements made to each individual's total intake of vitamins A, C and D.

Table 14.1 Average daily intakes of energy and vitamins A, C and D from food types for infants who were receiving vitamin supplements (Y) and those who were non-supplement users (N)

Food types	Energy (kcal)		Vitamin A (µg)		Vitamin C (mg)		Vitamin D (µg)	
	Y	N	Y	N	Y	N	Y	N
Commercial infant foods	153	144	104	88	65	59	0.41	0.34
Breast milk	37	29	32	25	2	1	0.01	0.00
Infant formulas	110	143	174	227	13	18	2.25	2.95
Cows milk	216	187	150	126	5	4	0.12	0.11
Family foods	351	366	309	296	15	16	0.36	0.36
Total	**867**	**870**	**768**	**762**	**101**	**99**	**3.14**	**3.77**

Table 14.2 Daily intake of vitamins A, C and D from supplements and their percentage contribution to the total amongst supplement users

	Number	Vitamin A		Vitamin C		Vitamin D	
		µg	Percentage of total	mg	Percentage of total	µg	Percentage of total
6–9 months	121	142	16.7	14	13.9	4.96	57.8
9–12 months	92	144	18.5	14	21.4	5.05	70.4

Supplementation with vitamins A, C and D is recommended for all infants from six months up to at least two years and preferably five years (DHSS, 1988). In this survey the vitamin A and C supplement was largely unnecessary as food alone provided more than the RNI. Indeed, the intakes of supplement users might be considered to be excessive. However, this was not the case with vitamin D. Intakes of vitamin D from food alone, on average met only 50% of the RNI. Intakes were lower in the older infants (mean 2.14µg, median 0.95µg). In infants fed only 'family foods' average intakes were less than one quarter (22%) of the RNI. Few foods are naturally rich in vitamin D. Indeed on average over 80% of the food vitamin D came from fortified infant foods and infant formula.

A dietary source of vitamin D may be unnecessary as the entire infant requirement could be synthesised by the action of ultra-violet radiation, primarily summer sunlight, on the uncovered skin. However, quantification of the contribution that sunlight makes to vitamin D intake is difficult. Department of Health therefore recommends a dietary intake of 7µg for infants as a safeguard (DH, 1991). In this survey the intakes of infants receiving vitamin supplements (total vitamin D intake: mean 8.96µg, median 7.93µg) met the RNI. However, over half of the infants did not receive vitamin supplements.

15 | Variation in food and nutrient intakes between regional groups

Average intakes for most nutrients were greater for infants from both Scotland and Northern England and for Wales, Midlands and the SW compared with those from SE, E Anglia and London.

Intakes of energy ($p < 0.05$), fat ($p < 0.05$), sodium ($p < 0.05$), chloride ($p < 0.05$), pantothenic acid ($p < 0.05$) and saturated fatty acids ($p < 0.05$) were significantly lower for infants from SE, E Anglia and London compared with the other two regional groups.

Infants from Scotland and Northern England also had significantly greater intakes of calcium ($p < 0.05$), iron ($p < 0.05$), manganese ($p < 0.05$), vitamin D ($p < 0.05$), thiamin ($p < 0.01$), niacin ($p < 0.05$), vitamin B_6 ($p < 0.01$), sucrose ($p < 0.05$), and those from Wales, Midlands and SW had markedly higher intakes of starch ($p < 0.01$), carbohydrate ($p < 0.01$) and monounsaturated fatty acids ($p < 0.025$) compared with those from SE, E Anglia and London.

Fructose and glucose intakes were significantly greater ($p < 0.05$) for infants from SE, E Anglia and London compared with those from the other regional groups.

Intakes of biotin and maltose were significantly greater ($p < 0.05$) for infants from Scotland and Northern England compared with those from Wales, Midlands and SW.

The contributions made by food types to the total intake of selected nutrients for the different regional groups are presented in Table 15.1. There are few regional differences in the range of foods fed to infants. Infants from the SE, E Anglia and London on average consumed fewer biscuits, cakes, puddings and confectionery compared with those from the other regional groups, which contributed to their smaller intake of fat and energy. Rusks were more popular among infants from Wales, Midlands, SW, Scotland and Northern England compared with those from SE, E Anglia and London and together with infant formulas were largely responsible for the difference in iron intakes. Infants from SE, E Anglia and London consumed more infant fruit juices and therefore had, on average, higher intakes of vitamin C and fructose than those from the other regions.

Regional differences are probably insignificant when other variables such as age, socioeconomic class, sex and presence of siblings are considered.

Table 15.1 Contribution of food types to selected nutrient intakes by regional groups

Nutrient	Unit	SE, E Anglia and London	Wales, Midlands and SW	Scotland and Northern England
Energy	kcal	836	899	871
of which				
—commercial infant food	kcal	151	133	157
—breast milk	kcal	41	43	15
—infant formulas	kcal	115	121	148
—cows milk	kcal	201	200	199
—'family foods'	kcal	328	404	353
(biscuits, cakes, puddings)	kcal	39	65	54
(confectionery)	kcal	7	13	14
Fat	g	33.9	36.9	35.9
of which				
—commercial infant food	g	2.9	2.8	3.1
—breast milk	g	2.5	2.6	0.9
—infant formulas	g	6.0	6.0	7.5
—cows milk	g	11.3	11.3	11.3
—'family foods'	g	11.2	14.2	13.1
(biscuits, cakes, puddings)	g	1.7	2.8	2.3
(confectionery)	g	0.1	0.6	0.7
Calcium	mg	752	796	799
of which				
—commercial infant food	mg	145	138	154
—breast milk	mg	21	21	8
—infant formulas	mg	84	107	124
—cows milk	mg	355	347	342
—'family foods'	mg	147	182	171
(cakes and puddings)	mg	14	23	24
Iron	mg	7.5	8.2	8.5
of which				
—commercial infant food	mg	3.91	4.09	4.43
(rusks)	mg	0.96	1.66	1.51
—breast milk	mg	0.04	0.04	0.02
—infant formulas	mg	1.19	1.34	1.59
—cows milk	mg	0.17	0.19	0.19
—'family foods'	mg	2.23	2.58	2.26
Vitamin C	mg	109	87	103
of which				
—commercial infant food	mg	74	43	67
(infant fruit juices/drinks)	mg	45	21	37
—milks (cows, breast, formulas)	mg	20	22	24
—'family foods'	mg	15	22	12
Fructose	g	7.3	6.2	6.1
of which				
—commercial infant food	g	4.0	2.3	3.4
(infant fruit juices/drinks)	g	2.4	1.5	1.9
—'family foods'	g	3.3	3.9	2.7

16 Variation in food and nutrient intakes between infants consuming different types of milk as their main milk

The Panel on Child Nutrition of the Committee on Medical Aspects of Food Policy (COMA) (DHSS, 1988) advice on milks considered suitable for inclusion in the diet from six months are breast milk, infant formulas, follow-on milks and whole pasteurised cows milk. Skimmed and semi-skimmed milks are not recommended because of their low energy density and vitamin A content (DHSS, 1988). In this survey 56 infants (11% of the sample) consumed some skimmed or semi-skimmed milk (low fat milks) during the seven day recording period. For 33 infants low fat milks were not the main milk, and for 16 of these infants low fat milks contributed 10% or less to their total milk consumption. This level of consumption is likely to be of little nutritional significance. However, for 15 infants the sole source of milk during the seven day recording period was low fat milk and, for a further eight, low fat milks were the main milk type. Table 16.1 shows the main types of milk consumed. The intake of selected nutrients for these infants is shown in Table 16.2 and is compared to intakes for infants whose main milk was whole cows milk (55%), infant formula (31%), or breast milk (10%). However, comparisons are complicated by the fact that infants consuming breast milk or infant formula as their main milk tended to be younger than infants consuming cows milk or low fat milk as their main milk. The numbers of infants consuming breast milk or low fat milk as their main milk were also low. Furthermore breast milk was not measured directly but consumption was estimated from the number and duration of feeds (Appendix V). The results from these groups should therefore be treated with some caution.

The fat and energy intake of infants whose main milk was low fat milk tended to be lower than for infants whose main milk was whole cows milk or infant formula. Average intake of vitamin A was 870µg (median 779µg) and 752µg (median 670µg) for infants fed low fat milk or whole cows milk respectively. Additional vitamin A was derived from vitamin supplements for 35% of infants whose main milk was low fat milk, compared with 48% of those whose main milk was whole cows milk.

The energy intake of infants consuming breast milk as their main milk was lower than for infants fed cows milk or infant formula. The difference may be real, reflecting the fact that they tended to be younger infants, or may be an artefact of the method of estimating breast milk consumption. Estimated average intakes of calcium, iron, zinc, energy, and vitamin D were below the RNIs. Over 70% of these infants had iron intakes below the RNI with a quarter below the LRNI. Almost all (94%) the infants fed breast milk as their main

Table 16.1 Main type of milk consumed

	Number	%	Proportion of consumers aged under 40 weeks (%)
Cows milk	267	55	38
Infant formula	150	31	76
Breast milk	48	10	77
Low fat milk	23	5	26

Table 16.2 Average daily intakes of selected nutrients by predominant milk type

Nutrient	Cows milk (n=267)		Breast milk (n=48)		Infant formula (n=150)		Low fat milk (n=23)	
	Mean	SD	Mean	SD	Mean	SD	Mean	SD
Protein (g)	34.8	8.4	21.0	6.2	26.2	7.5	34.2	7.5
Fat (g)	37.5	10.1	30.9	6.4	35.3	11.8	25.2	6.5
Calcium (mg)	880	255	512	161	689	200	823	220
Iron (mg)	6.7	3.3	6.4	2.7	11.3	4.0	7.1	3.7
Zinc (mg)	4.7	1.1	3.6	0.8	4.5	1.2	4.7	1.2
Retinol (µg)	462	368	519	503	801	323	657	977
Carotene (µg)	1250	915	844	551	961	745	900	521
Vitamin D (µg)	1.0	0.9	1.0	0.8	9.1	3.8	0.8	0.5
Vitamin C (mg)	85	80	76	39	135	76	96	96
Energy (kcal)	901	200	718	135	871	233	793	143
Energy (MJ)	3.79	0.84	3.02	0.57	3.66	0.98	3.35	0.60

milk had zinc intakes below the RNI, with just under a quarter of these falling below the LRNI. However, zinc absorption from human milk has been shown to be higher than from cows milk and cows milk based infant formulas (Sandstrom et al., 1983). Protein intake was on average lower in infants consuming breast milk. However, protein from breast milk has a higher biological value than protein in a mixed diet.

On average infants consuming infant formula as their main milk had the highest intakes of several nutrients, notably iron, retinol, vitamin C and vitamin D. Indeed, in this group, intakes of vitamin D from food met the RNI (129%). This reflects both the fortification of infant formula and high consumption of fortified infant foods by this group.

Over 70% of infants consuming whole cows milk and 65% of infants given mainly low fat milks as their main milk had iron intakes below the RNI compared with 21% of those who were fed infant formulas. In our study, infants whose predominant type of milk was cows milk, breast milk or low fat milks had significantly lower iron intakes than those fed infant formulas. No infant fed infant formulas as their main milk had an average iron intake below the LRNI whereas just over one fifth of those receiving whole cows milk (21%) or low fat milks (22%) had intakes below the LRNI. Amongst the small number of infants receiving breast milk as their main milk, one quarter had intakes below the LRNI for iron.

Table 16.3 Average daily intakes of vitamins A, C, and D amongst infants receiving vitamin supplements (n=213)

Predominant milk type	Number given supplements	Average intakes of vitamin A			Average intakes of vitamin C			Average intakes of vitamin D		
		Food only (µg)	Supplements only (µg)	Percentage of total from supplements	Food only (mg)	Supplements only (mg)	Percentage of total from supplements	Food only (µg)	Supplements only (µg)	Percentage of total from supplements
Cows milk	128	673	172	22	92	17	23	1.10	6.02	81
Infant formulas	56	969	172	17	131	17	13	8.89	6.03	42
Breast milk	21	820	125	16	91	13	13	1.05	4.38	64
Low fat milk	8	750	146	21	78	15	21	0.90	5.10	76

References

Black, A. E., Billewicz, W. Z. and Thomson, A. M. (1976). The diets of preschool children in Newcastle upon Tyne 1968–71. *Br. J. Nutr.* 35, 105–113.

Black, A. E., Cole, T. J., Wiles, S. J. and White, F. (1983). Daily variation in food intake of infants from 2 to 18 months. *Hum. Nutr: Appl. Nutr.* 37A, 448–458.

Dallman, P. R. (1986). Iron deficiency in the weanling: a nutritional problem on the way to resolution. *Acta. Paediatr. Scand. Suppl.* 323, 59–67.

Department of Health and Social Security (1975). *A nutritional survey of pre-school children, 1967–68.* Report on Health and Social Subjects No. 10. London: HMSO.

Department of Health and Social Security (1979). *Recommended amounts of food energy and nutrients for groups of people in the United Kingdom.* Report on Health and Social Subjects No. 15. London: HMSO.

Department of Health and Social Security (1988). *Present day practice in infant feeding: third report.* Report on Health and Social Subjects No. 32. London: HMSO.

Department of Health (1989a). *The diets of British schoolchildren.* Report on Health and Social Subjects No. 36. London: HMSO.

Department of Health (1989b). *Dietary sugars and human disease.* Report on Health and Social Subjects No. 37. London: HMSO.

Department of Health (1991). *Dietary Reference Values for food energy and nutrients for the United Kingdom.* Report on Health and Social Subjects No. 41. London: HMSO.

FAO/WHO (1967). Requirements of vitamin A, thiamin, riboflavin and niacin. *WHO Tech. Rep. Ser.* 362.

Fairweather-Tait, S. J. (1989). Iron in food and its availability. *Acta Paediatr. Scand. Suppl.* 361, 12–20.

Gregory, J., Foster, K., Tyler, H. and Wiseman, M. (1990). *The dietary and nutritional survey of British adults.* London: HMSO.

Holland, B., Unwin, I. D. and Buss, D. H. (1988). *Cereal and cereal products. The third supplement to McCance and Widdowson's The composition of foods,* 4th edn. Royal Society of Chemistry.

Horwitt, M. K., Harvey, C. C., Rothwell, W. S., Culter, J. L. and Haffron, D. (1956). Tryptophan-niacin relationships in man. Studies with diets deficient in riboflavin and niacin, together with observations on the excretion of nitrogen and niacin metabolites. *J. Nutr.* 60. (suppl 1), 1–43.

Kjaernes, U. Bolten, G., Lande, B. and Nilsson, D. (1988). Food intake and patterns of feeding of Norwegian infants. *Eur. J. Clin. Nutr.* 42, 249–260.

McKillop, F. M. and Durnin, J. V. G. A. (1982). The energy and nutrient intake of a random sample (305) of infants. *Hum. Nutr: Appl. Nutr.* 36A, 405–421.

McNally, E., Hendricks, S. and Horowitz, I. (1985). A look at breast-feeding trends in Canada (1963–1982). *Can. J. of Public Health* 76 (2), 101–7.

Martin J. (1978). *Infant feeding 1975: attitudes and practice in England and Wales.* London: HMSO.

Martin, J. and Monk, J. (1982). *Infant feeding 1980.* London: HMSO.

Martin, J. and White, A. (1988). *Infant feeding 1985* London: HMSO.

Office of Population Censuses and Surveys (1989). *General household survey 1986.* London: HMSO.

Paul, A. A., Black, A. E., Evans, J., Cole, T. J. and Whitehead, R. G. (1988). Breastmilk intake and growth in infants from two to ten months. *J. Hum. Nutr. and Diet.* 1, 437–450.

Paul, A. A., and Southgate, D. A. T. (1978). *McCance and Widdowson's The composition of foods*, 4th edn. London: HMSO.

Sandstrom, B., Keen, C. L. and Lonnerdal, B. (1983). An experimental model for studies of zinc bioavailability from milk and infant formulas using extrinsic labelling. *Am. J. Clin. Nutr.* 38, 420–28.

Tan, S. P., Wenlock, R. W. and Buss, D. H. (1985). *Immigrant Foods. Second supplement to McCance and Widdowson's The composition of foods*, 4th edn. London: HMSO.

Whitehead, R. G., Paul, A. A. and Ahmed, E. A. (1986). Weaning practices in the UK and variations in anthropometric development. *Acta. Paediatr. Scand. Suppl.* 323, 14–23.

Whitehead, R. G. and Paul, A. A. (1987). Changes in infant feeding in Britain during the last century. In: *Infant nutrition and cardiovascular disease.* Southampton: MRC Environment Epidemiology Unit (Scientific report, No. 8).

Wilkinson, P. W. and Davies, D. P. (1978) When and why are babies weaned? *Br. Med. J.* 1, 1682–1683.

Banana measuring guide

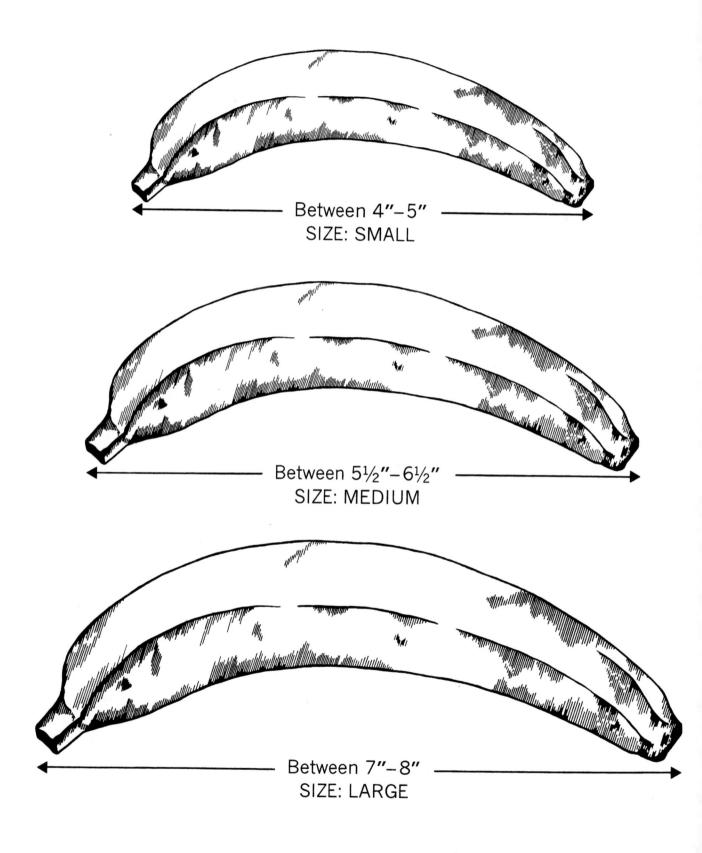

Between 4″–5″
SIZE: SMALL

Between 5½″–6½″
SIZE: MEDIUM

Between 7″–8″
SIZE: LARGE

APPENDIX II **Food diary**

JOB NUMBER

JN 4389

PANEL NUMBER

BABY FEEDING SURVEY

DAILY FEEDING DIARY

DAY :

- Please fill in this diary each time you give your baby anything to eat or drink today, starting with the first item after one o'clock in the morning - for example, a milk feed at 2 am or breakfast at 7 am.

- Please record each item on a separate line, and be sure to note down all items of food or drink, whether given at mealtimes or as a snack between meals, and whether at home or away.

- Please measure the amount your baby eats or drinks as accurately as you can, using the jug or scoop provided if appropriate.

BEFORE COMPLETING THE DIARY, PLEASE READ THE SEPARATE WRITTEN INSTRUCTIONS.

SECTION A	ALL MANUFACTURED BABY FOODS (ie. THOSE FOODS SOLD SPECIALLY FOR BABIES)

ALL TINS, JARS, PACKETS OF BABY FOODS INCLUDING CEREALS, MEAT, FISH, EGG, CHEESE AND VEGETABLE DISHES, PUDDINGS, RUSKS ETC.

A1 TINS/JARS FULL FLAVOUR DESCRIPTION (AS ON CONTAINER)	BRAND OR MANUFACTURER	TYPE OF FOOD eg. Strained/ Junior/Stage I	TYPE OF CONTAINER Please tick		SIZE OF TIN/JAR IN GRAMMES	AMOUNT EATEN BY BABY How much of tin/jar was eaten eg. all,½, ¼ etc
			TIN	JAR		

A2 ALL DRIED OR INSTANT MANUFACTURED BABY FOODS WHICH ARE MIXED WITH LIQUID BEFORE SERVING (including granulated rusks)

FULL FLAVOUR DESCRIPTION (AS ON CONTAINER)	BRAND OR MANUFACTURER	HOW MANY SCOOPS OF DRIED FOOD USED ?	WHAT WAS IT MIXED WITH ? If milk, juice, etc please describe type	AMOUNT OF LIQUID ADDED IN ML OR FL OZ.	AMOUNT OF MADE-UP FOOD EATEN BY BABY eg. all,½, ¼ etc

A3 RUSKS BRAND AND FULL FLAVOUR DESCRIPTION (AS ON CONTAINER)	WAS RUSK EATEN DRY OR MIXED WITH LIQUID ? Please write in	HOW MANY RUSKS MIXED ?	IF MIXED WITH LIQUID: WHAT WAS RUSK MIXED WITH ? If milk, juice etc, please describe type	AMOUNT OF LIQUID ADDED IN ML OR FL OZ	AMOUNT EATEN BY BABY: IF DRY HOW MANY UNITS ? eg ½, 1, 2 etc	IF MIXED HOW MUCH OF MIXTURE ? eg. all,½, ¼ etc

SECTION B	ALL MILK GIVEN TO BABY (including milk poured on other foods eg. puddings, breakfast cereals)				
TIME GIVEN Please write in time milk was given	BREAST MILK	FORMULA MILK ie. baby milk made up from powder		OTHER LIQUID MILK eg. Cows milk – silver top, skimmed, evaporated; goats milk etc	
	NO. OF MINUTES FEEDING	FULL DESCRIPTION OF MILK (AS ON CONTAINER)	AMOUNT DRUNK IN ML. OR FL. OZ.	FULL DESCRIPTION OF MILK	AMOUNT DRUNK IN ML. OR FL. OZ.

SECTION C	ALL OTHER DRINKS eg. WATER, SQUASH, FRUIT JUICE, SYRUP, TEA, LEMONADE, DRINKING CHOCOLATE, HORLICKS etc					
TIME GIVEN Please write in time drink was given	BRAND AND FULL DESCRIPTION OF DRINK (AS ON CONTAINER) eg. Delrosa syrup, Tesco unsweetened orange juice, tea with milk, instant Horlicks, cocoa made with milk, etc	DID YOU DILUTE DRINK WITH WATER ? Please tick below		DID YOU ADD SUGAR ? Please tick below		AMOUNT DRUNK IN ML. OR FL. OZ
		YES	NO	YES	NO	

JN 4389 BABY FEEDING SURVEY

SECTION D	ALL OTHER FOODS, WHICH ARE NOT ONLY FOR BABIES

BREAKFAST CEREALS (NOT BABY CEREALS) Please write in type/brand eg. Weetabix, Cornflakes, Readybrek etc	DID YOU ADD MILK ? Please tick below YES	NO	DID YOU ADD SUGAR ? Please tick below YES	NO	AMOUNT EATEN No. of scoops OR No. of units

BREAD Tick which type: WHITE	WHOLEMEAL	OTHER BROWN	SIZE OF LOAF SMALL	LARGE	HOW BREAD SERVED Please tick below FRESH	TOASTED	FRIED	SPREAD WITH WHAT ? Please write in eg. butter and Marmite, margarine and honey etc	AMOUNT EATEN eg. ½ slice, 1 slice etc

FRUIT/VEGETABLES eg. apple, banana (STATE SIZE), peas, potatoes, carrots, etc	WHAT TYPE ? ie. fresh, frozen tinned, dried	HOW PREPARED ? RAW/NOT HEATED	BAKED/ BOILED/ HEATED	ROAST/ SAUTE	FRIED/ eg chips	HOW SERVED ? PUREED/ MASHED	CHOPPED	LEFT WHOLE	AMOUNT EATEN No. of scoops OR No. of units, ½ units etc

RICE/PASTA (excluding milk puddings-see below) eg. macaroni cheese, spaghetti hoops in tomato sauce, savoury rice etc	WHAT TYPE ? ie. dried, tinned, frozen	COOKING METHOD eg. boiled, heated, stir-fried etc.	AMOUNT EATEN No. of scoops

MEAT/FISH/POULTRY DISHES Please describe main ingredients eg. sausages, fish fingers, beef casserole, shepherds pie, roast chicken, etc.	HOW PREPARED ? STEWED/ CASSEROLED IN SAUCE	FRIED	ROAST/ BAKED/ GRILLED	IF CASSEROLE, DID IT CONTAIN VEG ? Please tick CARROTS	POTAT-OES	OTHER VEG	NO VEG	HOW SERVED ? PUREED/ MASHED	CHOPPED	LEFT WHOLE	AMOUNT EATEN No. of scoops OR No. of units eg. 2 fish fingers

GRAVY Complete one line for each serving, ticking all ingredients used	MEAT JUICES	WHAT INGREDIENTS WERE USED TO MAKE GRAVY ? Please tick STOCK CUBE eg Oxo	GRAVY MAKER eg. Bisto	FLOUR/CORNFLOUR	AMOUNT EATEN No. of scoops

EGGS/EGG DISHES eg. boiled egg, cheese omelette, scrambled egg, quiche etc	COOKING METHOD Please describe	AMOUNT EATEN No. of scoops OR How much of yolk/white ?

CHEESE/CHEESE DISHES eg. grated cheese, cauliflower cheese, etc	TYPE OF CHEESE eg. cottage cheese, cheddar, etc	AMOUNT EATEN No. of scoops OR No. of ounces

MILK DISHES AND MILK BASED SAUCES eg. rice pudding, custard DESCRIBE BELOW	WHAT TYPE OF DISH ? Please tick MILK PUDDING	CUSTARD (USING EGGS)	CUSTARD (USING POWDER)	MILK-BASED SAUCES	OTHER	AMOUNT EATEN No. of scoops

YOGHURT (not Baby Yoghurt - see Section A) DESCRIBE BRAND/TYPE/FLAVOUR BELOW	CARTON SIZE (IN GRAMMES)	DID YOU ADD SUGAR ? YES	NO	AMOUNT EATEN No.of scoops OR How much of carton ?

ANY OTHER TYPES OF FOOD EATEN TODAY EITHER WITH MEAL OR AS A SNACK eg. soup, biscuits, crisps, sweets, ice-cream

FULL DESCRIPTION OF ITEM eg. tinned tomato soup, Rich Tea biscuit, scone with butter	AMOUNT EATEN No. of scoops/ OR units	FULL DESCRIPTION OF ITEM	AMOUNT EATEN No. of scoops OR units

Questionnaire

RESEARCH SURVEYS OF GREAT BRITAIN LIMITED, RESEARCH CENTRE, WEST GATE, LONDON, W5 1EL.   TELEPHONE : 01 - 997 5555

BABY FEEDING SURVEY

PANEL NUMBER	SERIAL NUMBER	CARD	JOB NUMBER	INTERVIEWER NUMBER
(1) (2) (3) (4) (5) (6)	(7) (8) (9)	(10)	(11) (12) (13) (14)	(15) (16) (17) (18) (19)
		2	4 3 8 9	

RESPONDENT'S NAME: _____	INTERVIEWER NAME
ADDRESS: _____	
_____	DATE OF INTERVIEW
_____	
_____	LENGTH OF INTERVIEW
_____	(20) (21)
TELEPHONE NUMBER: _____	WRITE IN _ _ _ _ _ _ _ _ MINUTES

* **INTERVIEWER: BEFORE STARTING INTERVIEW, COLLECT AND INSPECT DIARY** *

		CODE	ROUTE
	Now I'd just like to ask you a few general questions about ..... (BABY'S NAME) and how you feed him/her.		
Q.1	First of all, can I just check how you fed .... (BABY'S NAME) the first week or two after he/she was born ?	(22)	
	BREAST ONLY	1	
	BOTTLE ONLY	2	Q.2
	BREAST AND BOTTLE	3	
Q.2	And are you now feeding ...... (BABY'S NAME) with breast milk only, "bottle" milk only or both breast and "bottle" ?		
	INTERVIEWER: "BOTTLE" MILK INCLUDES ALL TYPES OF MILK OTHER THAN BREAST, WHETHER FED FROM BOTTLE OR CUP.	(23)	
	BREAST ONLY	1	
	"BOTTLE" ONLY	2	SEE
	BREAST AND BOTTLE	3	BELOW

INTERVIEWER: CHECK ROUTE

IF BABY HAS ALWAYS BEEN BREAST FED ONLY (CODE 1 AT Q.1 AND Q.2), SKIP TO Q.7.
IF BABY WAS BREAST FED AT ALL AT BIRTH (CODES 1 OR 3 AT Q.1) AND IS NOW BOTTLE ONLY (CODE 2 AT Q.2), ASK Q.3
IF BABY WAS BREAST FED ONLY AT BIRTH (CODE 1 AT Q.1) AND IS NOW BREAST AND BOTTLE, ASK Q.4
OTHERS GO TO Q.5.

			ROUTE
Q.3	How old was (BABY'S NAME) when you gave up breast feeding ?	(24 - 25)	
	WRITE IN NUMBER OF WEEKS (ASSUME 1 MONTH = 4 WEEKS) _ _ _ _ _ _ WEEKS ADD LEADING ZERO IF NECESSARY		Q.5
Q.4	How old was (BABY'S NAME) when you started bottle-feeding in combination with breast feeding ?	(26 - 27)	
	WRITE IN NUMBER OF WEEKS (ASSUME 1 MONTH = 4 WEEKS) _ _ _ _ _ _ WEEKS ADD LEADING ZERO IF NECESSARY		Q.5

		ROUTE
Q.5	Thinking back to the first bottle feeds you gave ...... (BABY'S NAME), what brand or type of milk did you use ? SHOW CARD A SINGLE CODE IN GRID BELOW	Q.6
Q.6	What brand or type of milk do you give ..... (BABY'S NAME) nowadays ? SHOW CARD A AGAIN CODE IN GRID BELOW	Q.7

		CODE (28)	ROUTE
Q.7	Have you given ..... (BABY'S NAME) any other brands of milk between now and the time he/she was born ? YES	1	Q.8
	NO	2	SEE Q.9

Q.8   What other brands of milk have you given him/her ?

SHOW CARD A AGAIN   CODE IN GRID BELOW

INTERVIEWER: IF UNCERTAIN, CODE AS 'OTHER' AND WRITE IN

	Q.5 BOTTLE MILK FIRST USED	Q.6 BOTTLE MILK NOW USED	Q.8 OTHER BOTTLE MILK GIVEN	ROUTE
INFANT FORMULA	(29)	(31)	(33)	
APTAMIL	1	1	1	
COW AND GATE PLUS	2	2	2	
COW AND GATE PREMIUM	3	3	3	
COW AND GATE FORMULA S	4	4	4	
MILUMIL	5	5	5	
MILUPA SPECIAL FORMULA	6	6	6	
OSTERFEED	7	7	7	
OSTERMILK NO.2	8	8	8	
OSTERMILK COMPLETE FORMULA	9	9	9	
PROGRESS	0	0	0	
PROSOBEE	X	X	X	
SMA GOLD CAP	A	A	A	SEE Q.9
	(30)	(32)	(34)	
SMA WHITE CAP	1	1	1	
WYSOY	2	2	2	
OTHER FORMULA	3	3	3	
OTHER MILKS				
COWS MILK - WHOLE (ie. silver top, gold top)	4	4	4	
COWS MILK - SEMI-SKIMMED	5	5	5	
COWS MILK - SKIMMED	6	6	6	
COWS MILK - EVAPORATED	7	7	7	
COWS MILK - CONDENSED	8	8	8	
GOATS MILK	9	9	9	
EWES MILK	0	0	0	
OTHER MILK (Code & Write In)				
Q.5 _____	X			
Q.6 _____		X		
Q.8 _____			X	

		CODE	ROUTE
	IF BABY HAS ANY BREAST FEEDS NOWADAYS (CODE 1 OR 3 AT Q.2), ASK Q.9 OTHERS SKIP TO Q.10	(35)	
Q.9	How many breast feeds a day does ..... (BABY'S NAME) usually have now ?		
	1	1	
	2	2	
	3	3	SEE Q.10
	4	4	
	5	5	
	6	6	
	7 OR MORE	7	

105

	CODE	ROUTE

IF BABY HAS ANY BOTTLE FEEDS NOWADAYS (CODE 2 OR 3 AT Q.2), ASK Q.10.   OTHERS SKIP TO Q.11

Q.10   How many bottle feeds a day does .... (BABY'S NAME) usually have now ?

	CODE (36)	ROUTE
1	1	
2	2	
3	3	
4	4	Q.11
5	5	
6	6	
7 OR MORE	7	

ASK ALL

Q.11   Now I'd like to ask you about introducing solid foods. What age was ...... when you first gave him/her any solid food ?

(37 - 38)

WRITE IN NUMBER OF WEEKS
(ASSUME 1 MONTH = 4 WEEKS)

ADD LEADING ZERO IF NECESSARY

Q.12

Q.12   What was the first kind of solid food he/she ate ?   SHOW CARD B

ONE CODE ONLY

	CODE (39)	
BABY RICE, FAREX	1	
OTHER BABY CEREAL	2	
RUSK/GRANULATED RUSK	3	
BREAD	4	
BANANA	5	
PUREED FRUIT (OTHER THAN BANANA)	6	
PUREED VEGETABLES	7	Q.13
EGG	8	
BABY YOGHURT	9	
INSTANT/STRAINED/STAGE 1 DINNER/BREAKFAST/SUPPER	0	
INSTANT/STRAINED/STAGE 1 PUDDING	X	
OTHER (Code & Write In)	A	

Q.13   And what was the next kind of solid food he/she ate ?   SHOW CARD B

ONE CODE ONLY

	CODE (40)	
BABY RICE, FAREX	1	
OTHER BABY CEREAL	2	
RUSK/GRANULATED RUSK	3	
BREAD	4	
BANANA	5	
PUREED FRUIT (OTHER THAN BANANA)	6	
PUREED VEGETABLES	7	Q.14
EGG	8	
BABY YOGHURT	9	
INSTANT/STRAINED/STAGE 1 DINNER/BREAKFAST/SUPPER	0	
INSTANT/STRAINED/STAGE 1 PUDDING	X	
OTHER (Code & Write In)	A	

	CODE	ROUTE

IF BABY CEREALS NOT MENTIONED AT Q.12/Q.13 (CODES 1 OR 2), ASK Q.14a.   OTHERS ASK Q.14b

Q.14a Has he/she ever eaten special baby cereals which you mix with liquid ?

(41)

YES	1	Q.14b
NO	2	Q.15a

Q.14b What liquid did you add when you _first_ gave him/her baby cereal ?

ONE CODE ONLY

(42)

FORMULA MILK	1	
OTHER MILK	2	
FRUIT JUICE	3	Q.14c
WATER	4	
OTHER (Code & Write In)	5	

_____

Q.14c Did you .....

(43)

MIX THE CEREAL WITH A LARGE QUANTITY OF LIQUID AND FEED FROM A BOTTLE	1	
OR MIX IT WITH A SMALL QUANTITY OF LIQUID AND FEED FROM A SPOON ?	2	Q.15a

Q.15a Has he/she ever had any drinks other than milk or water ?

IF "YES", ASK: How old was he/she when he/she _first_ started to have other kinds of drinks ?

WRITE IN AGE BELOW

HAS NEVER HAD OTHER DRINKS	A	Q.17

(44 - 45)

WRITE IN AGE IN WEEKS   Q.15b

(ASSUME 1 MONTH = 4 WEEKS)

ADD LEADING ZERO IF NECESSARY

Q.15b And what kind of drink was that _first_ drink ?   SHOW CARD C

ONE CODE ONLY

CODE

(46)

BABY SYRUP (eg. Delrosa, Baby Ribena Syrup)	1	
BABY FRUIT JUICE (ready-to-drink)	2	
CONCENTRATED BABY FRUIT JUICE (eg. Boots, Nusoft)	3	
OTHER PURE FRUIT JUICE (ready-to-drink)	4	
CONCENTRATED POWDERED DRINK (eg. Milupa)	5	Q.16a
ORDINARY FRUIT SQUASH OR CONCENTRATE (needs to be diluted eg. ordinary Ribena, Orange Squash etc)	6	
OTHER (Code & Write In)	7	

Q.16a And what kind of drinks does he/she have most often nowadays ?

SHOW CARD C   ONE CODE ONLY

(47)

BABY SYRUP (eg. Delrosa, Baby Ribena Syrup)	1	
BABY FRUIT JUICE (ready-to-drink)	2	
CONCENTRATED BABY FRUIT JUICE (eg. Boots, Nusoft)	3	
OTHER PURE FRUIT JUICE (ready-to-drink)	4	
CONCENTRATED POWDERED DRINK (eg. Milupa)	5	Q.16b
ORDINARY FRUIT SQUASH OR CONCENTRATE (needs to be diluted eg. ordinary Ribena, Orange Squash etc)	6	
OTHER (Code & Write In)	7	

		CODE	ROUTE
Q.16b	Do you dilute this drink with water ?		
	IF "YES", ASK: How many parts of water do you normally add to one part of the drink ?	(48)	
	NO, NOT DILUTED	A	

(49 - 50)

WRITE IN NUMBER OF PARTS OF WATER
ADDED TO ONE PART OF DRINK

Q.17

ADD LEADING ZERO IF NECESSARY

SHOW CARD D

	CODE
Q.17 Thinking now about what he/she eats at present, can you tell me which, if any, of these types of foods specially prepared for babies he/she eats nowadays ?	(51)
STRAINED/STAGE I SAVOURY MEALS	1
STRAINED/STAGE I PUDDINGS/DESSERTS	2
JUNIOR/STAGE II SAVOURY MEALS	3
JUNIOR/STAGE II PUDDINGS/DESSERTS	4
INSTANT SAVOURY MEALS	5
INSTANT PUDDINGS/DESSERTS	6
BABY CEREALS	7
BABY YOGHURT	8
RUSKS	9
OTHER SPECIAL BABY FOODS (Code & Write In)	0
NO SPECIAL BABY FOODS	X

Q.18a (route for above)

		CODE	ROUTE
Q.18a	Does he/she eat any ordinary food, like the food which you cook for the rest of the family ?	(52)	
	YES	1	Q.18b
	NO	2	Q.20

		CODE	ROUTE
Q.18b	Thinking about the way you prepare ordinary food to give him/her do you normally ... SINGLE CODE	(53)	
	USE EXACTLY THE SAME RECIPES AS FOR THE REST OF THE FAMILY	1	Q.20
	USE SIMILAR RECIPES BUT CHANGE OR LEAVE OUT SOME INGREDIENTS	2	Q.19
	OR USE DIFFERENT RECIPES ESPECIALLY FOR YOUR BABY ?	3	

		CODE	ROUTE
Q.19	In what way are the recipes you use for him/her different from those you use for the rest of the family ? DO NOT READ OUT	(54)	
	LEAVE OUT/DO NOT ADD SALT	1	
	LEAVE OUT/DO NOT ADD SUGAR	2	
	LEAVE OUT/DO NOT ADD CURRY POWDER, CHILLI, SPICES, STRONG FLAVOURS	3	Q.20
	OTHER DIFFERENCES (Code & Write In)	4	

108

SHOW CARD E FOR Q.20 - Q.21d

Q.20   Which of these types of ordinary cooked and ready-to-use foods, <u>not</u> eaten only by babies, does he/she eat at present ?   <u>CODE IN GRID BELOW</u>

Q.21a   Which of these foods do you normally add <u>salt</u> to if you are cooking or preparing them for him/her ?

<u>CODE IN GRID BELOW</u>   PROMPT MOTHER FOR ALL RELEVANT FOODS CODED AT Q.20

Q.21b   And which of these foods do you normally add <u>sugar</u> to, if you are cooking or preparing them for him/her ?

<u>CODE IN GRID BELOW</u>   PROMPT MOTHER FOR ALL RELEVANT FOODS CODED AT Q.20

Q 21c   Are there any of these types of meat from which you usually try to remove some of the <u>fat before</u> they are cooked ?

<u>CODE IN GRID BELOW</u>   PROMPT MOTHER FOR ALL RELEVANT FOODS CODED AT Q.20

Q.21d   Are there any of these types of meat from which you usually try to remove some of the fat <u>after</u> they are cooked ?

<u>CODE IN GRID</u>

	Q.20 FOODS BABY EATS	Q.21a ADD SALT	Q.21b ADD SUGAR	Q.21c REMOVE FAT <u>BEFORE</u> COOKING	Q.21d REMOVE FAT <u>AFTER</u> COOKING	ROUTE
READY TO USE FOODS	(55)	(57)	(59)	(61)	(63)	
BISCUITS	1					
BREAKFAST CEREALS (<u>not</u> only for babies)	2		2			
BREAD/TOAST	3					
POTATO CRISPS	4					
SWEETS/CHOCOLATES	5					
YOGHURT (not baby yoghurt)	6		6			
COOKED OR PREPARED FOODS						
FRESH OR COOKED FRUIT	7		7			
POTATOES	8	8				
OTHER VEGETABLES	9	9				
RICE/PASTA	0	0				
BACON AND HAM	X	X		X	X	
ROAST OR GRILLED MEAT OR POULTRY	A	A		A	A	Q.22
	(56)	(58)	(60)	(62)	(64)	
MINCE AND DISHES MADE WITH MINCE	1	1			1	
OTHER POULTRY DISHES & CASSEROLES	2	2		2	2	
OTHER MEAT DISHES & CASSEROLES	3	3		3	3	
LIVER AND DISHES MADE WITH LIVER	4	4				
FISH AND DISHES MADE WITH FISH	5	5				
EGG YOLK	6	6				
EGG WHITE	7	7				
DISHES MADE WITH WHOLE EGG (eg. scrambled egg)	8	8				
CHEESE AND CHEESE DISHES	9	9				
MILK BASED DISHES (eg. rice pudding, custard, sauces)	0		0			
OTHER PUDDINGS	X		X			
NONE OF THESE	A					

109

Q.22   What kind of pans do you normally use when you cook or heat food for ...... ?

	CODE	ROUTE

INTERVIEWER: PROBE TO ESTABLISH TYPE OF COOKING SURFACE ie. <u>INSIDE</u>
OF PAN. CONFIRM BY INSPECTION IF POSSIBLE.

	CODE	ROUTE
	(65)	
NON-STICK COATED	1	
PYREX/HEAT-PROOF GLASS	2	
ENAMEL	3	
COPPER	4	SEE
STAINLESS STEEL	5	Q.23
ALUMINIUM	6	
'SILVER' METAL, NOT SURE IF STAINLESS STEEL OR ALUMINIUM	7	
OTHER (Please specify)	8	

<u>IF BABY EATS BREAD/TOAST (CODED 3 AT Q.20), ASK Q.23.</u>   <u>OTHERS SKIP TO Q.24</u>

Q.23a When you give ..... bread or toast, do you normally use a sliced loaf, or bread which you
cut yourself ?

	CODE	ROUTE
	(66)	
SLICED	1	
CUT MYSELF	2	Q.23b

Q.23b How thick are the slices usually ?

	CODE	ROUTE
	(67)	
THICK (equivalent to 'thick-sliced' loaf)	1	
MEDIUM (equivalent to 'medium-sliced' loaf)	2	
THIN (equivalent to 'thin-sliced' loaf)	3	Q.23c
EXTRA-THIN (thinner than a 'thin-sliced' loaf)	4	

Q.23c Do you usually cut off the crust or not ?

	CODE	ROUTE
	(68)	
YES	1	Q.23d
NO	2	

Q.23d Do you ever spread the bread with butter, margarine or a similar product, such as
low-fat spread ?

	CODE	ROUTE
	(69)	
YES	1	Q.23e
NO	2	Q.24

	CODE	ROUTE
Q.23e What brand and type of spread do you normally use ?		
SHOW CARD F	(70)	
BUTTER SALTED	1	
UNSALTED	2	
HARD MARGARINE (in blocks) ECHO	3	
FRESH FIELDS	4	
KRONA	5	
STORK	6	
SUMMER COUNTY	7	
TOMOR, BLOCK MARGARINE	8	
OWN BRAND BLOCK	9	
SOFT MARGARINE (in tubs)		
BANQUET	0	
BLUE BAND	X	
CAROUSEL	A	
	(71)	
KRAFT SUPERFINE	1	
LUXURY SOFT	2	
STORK SB	3	
OWN BRAND SOFT	4	
POLYUNSATURATED MARGARINE (in tubs)		
CWS GOODLIFE	5	
FLORA	6	
KRAFT POLYUNSATURATED	7	
SOYA	8	Q.24
SUNFLOWER	9	
VITALITE	0	
VITAQUELLE	X	
OWN BRAND POLYUNSATURATED	A	
YELLOW SPREADS (in tubs)	(72)	
CLOVER	1	
GOLDEN CHURN	2	
GOLDEN VALE	3	
MEADOWCUP	4	
LOW-FAT SPREADS (in tubs)		
DELIGHT	5	
GOLD	6	
OUTLINE	7	
OWN BRAND LOW FAT SPREAD	8	
DON'T KNOW TYPE/OTHER TYPE (Code & Write In Full Details)	9	

INTERVIEWER: IF RESPONDENT IS UNSURE, INSPECT IF POSSIBLE TO CONFIRM BRAND/TYPE.

111

		CODE	ROUTE
Q.24 Which, if any, of these extra vitamins or diet supplements do you give to ..... (BABY'S NAME) nowadays ? SHOW CARD G AND CODE ALL MENTIONED PROBE FOR ANY OTHER VITAMINS OR SUPPLEMENTS GIVEN		(73)	
	CHILDRENS VITAMIN DROPS	1	
	COD LIVER OIL	2	
	HALIBUT LIVER OIL	3	
	OTHER TYPE OF VITAMINS (Code & Write In)	4	SEE BELOW
	OTHER DIET SUPPLEMENT (Code & Write In)	5	

FOR EACH ITEM MENTIONED, ASK Q.25 - Q.27

		CODE	ROUTE
	NO VITAMINS OR SUPPLEMENTS GIVEN NOWADAYS	A	Q.28

Q.25 How do you obtain the ..... (TYPE OF ITEM) ?   CODE BELOW

Q.26 About how often do you give him/her the ...... ?   CODE BELOW

Q.27 How much ...... do you give him/her each time ?   CODE BELOW

PUNCHER: SKIP 74-80
START CARD 3
DUP 1 - 9
PUNCH 10/ 3

	CHILDREN'S VITAMIN DROPS	COD LIVER OIL	HALIBUT LIVER OIL	ANY OTHER TYPE OF VITAMINS	ANY OTHER DIET SUPPLEMENT
Q.25: HOW OBTAINED	(11)	(16)	(21)	(26)	(31)
GET ON PRESCRIPTION	1	1	1	1	1
GET FREE AT CLINIC	2	2	2	2	2
BUY AT CLINIC	3	3	3	3	3
BUY ELSEWHERE	4	4	4	4	4
OTHER (Code & Write In)	5	5	5	5	5
Q.26: HOW OFTEN GIVEN	(12)	(17)	(22)	(27)	(32)
EVERY DAY	7	7	7	7	7
SEVERAL TIMES A WEEK	8	8	8	8	8
ABOUT ONCE A WEEK	9	9	9	9	9
ABOUT ONCE A FORTNIGHT	0	0	0	0	0
ABOUT ONCE A MONTH	X	X	X	X	X
LESS OFTEN	A	A	A	A	A
Q.27: HOW MUCH EACH TIME	(13)	(18)	(23)	(28)	(33)
WRITE IN: NO. OF DROPS					
OR	(14)	(19)	(24)	(29)	(34)
NO. OF TABLETS					
OR	(15)	(20)	(25)	(30)	(35)
NO. OF TEASPOONS					

ROUTE: REPEAT Q.25 - Q.27 FOR EACH ITEM MENTIONED AT Q.24.   THEN GO TO Q.28

		CODE	ROUTE
Q.28 And now, can I just check on a few facts and figures about ...... (BABY'S NAME) ? What weight was he/she at birth?		(36)	
	LESS THAN 5lb	1	
	5lb - 5lb 15oz	2	
	6lb - 6lb 15oz	3	Q.29
	7lb - 7lb 15oz	4	
	MORE THAN 8lb	5	

		CODE	ROUTE
Q.29 And what is his/her weight now ?		(37)	
	LESS THAN 12lb	1	
	12lb - 14lb 15oz	2	
	15lb - 17lb 15oz	3	
	18lb - 20lb 15oz	4	Q.30
	21lb - 23lb 15oz	5	
	24lb - 26lb 15oz	6	
	MORE THAN 27lb	7	
Q.30 Has he/she ever had any serious illness ?		(38)	
	NO	1	
	YES (Please code & describe)	2	Q.31
	_____		
Q.31 And does he/she have any allergies or special needs which affect the kind of food he/she needs to have ?		(39)	
	NO	1	
	YES (Please code & describe type of allergy or special need and how diet is affected)	2	Q.32
	_____		
	_____		
SHOW CARD H		(40)	
Q.32 Which of the following activities can he/she do ?	SIT UP - WITH SUPPORT	1	
	SIT UP - UNSUPPORTED	2	
	CRAWL FORWARDS	3	
	CRAWL BACKWARDS	4	
	STAND UP - WITH SUPPORT	5	
	STAND UP - UNSUPPORTED	6	Q.33
	WALK - WITH SUPPORT	7	
	WALK - UNSUPPORTED	8	
	FEED HIMSELF OR HERSELF WITH FINGERS	9	
	FEED HIMSELF OR HERSELF WITH A SPOON	0	
	NONE OF THESE	X	
Q.33 How often do you find you need to wash his/her hands before a meal ?		(41)	
	ALWAYS/NEARLY ALWAYS	1	
	OFTEN/QUITE OFTEN	2	
	OCCASIONALLY	3	Q.34
	HARDLY EVER	4	
	NEVER	5	
Q.34 Finally, can I just check a few details about yourself. Do you have any paid employment at present ?		(42)	
	YES - FULL-TIME (30+ HOURS PER WEEK)	1	
	YES - PART-TIME (UP TO 30 HOURS PER WEEK)	2	Q.35
	NO PAID EMPLOYMENT	3	

113

	CODE	ROUTE
Q.35 What was your age when you finished full-time education ?		
	(43)	
LESS THAN 16	1	
16 - 17	2	
18 - 19	3	Q.36
20 - 22	4	
23+	5	
NOT YET FINISHED	6	
Q.36 Is ..... your only child ?		
INTERVIEWER: IF ANSWER KNOWN, CODE WITHOUT ASKING	(44)	
YES	1	THANK & CLOSE
NO	2	Q.37
Q.37 Can I just check the age/ages of your other child/children ?		
OTHER CHILD(REN) AGED	(45)	
0 UP TO 1	1	
1 UP TO 2	2	
2 UP TO 3	3	
3 UP TO 4	4	
4 UP TO 5	5	THANK &
5 UP TO 7	6	CLOSE
7 UP TO 10	7	
10 UP TO 12	8	
12 UP TO 16	9	
16+	0	

PUNCHER: SKIP 46 - 80

114

Panel sign up card

R S G B

T.S.G.B. LTD.,
RESEARCH CENTRE,
WEST GATE,
LONDON. W5 1EL
Tel. No. 01-997 5555

BABY PANEL
SIGN-UP CARD

PANEL NUMBER

(1 - 6)

MOTHERS NAME: ....

FULL POSTAL ADDRESS ....

TOWN: .... COUNTY: ....

TELEPHONE NUMBER: ....

OFFICE USE

YR/FT	(7 - 9)
CARD NO. 1	(10)
REGION	(11 - 14)

THE PANEL BABY		THE HOUSEHOLD
	(15)	
	(16)	DATES OF BIRTH AND SEX OF ANY OTHER CHILDREN UNDER 5 YEARS AT THE TIME OF SIGN-UP.
NAME	(17)	.... (28)
DATE OF BIRTH	(18)	.... (29)
DAY MONTH YEAR		
....	(19)	.... (30)

INCIDENCE OF BIRTH		(20)	TOTAL NUMBER OF PEOPLE IN THE HOUSEHOLD INCLUDING THE MOTHER AND PANEL BABY.	
	FIRST BABY	1		(31)
	SECOND BABY	2		
	THIRD BABY	3	2	2
	FOURTH OR LATER BABY	4	3	3
SINGLE/MULTIPLE BIRTH		(21)	4	4
	SINGLE BIRTH	1	5	5
	TWIN	2	6	6
	TRIPLET ETC.	3	7	7
		(22) SKIP	8+	8

OCCUPATION OF HEAD OF HOUSEHOLD:

.... (32)

SEX		(23)	SOCIAL CLASS	AB	1
	MALE	1		C1	2
	FEMALE	2		C2	3
				DE	4

THE MOTHER

AGE WHEN THE PANEL BABY WAS BORN		(24)	IN WHICH COUNTRY WERE YOU BORN ?		(33)
	15 - 17	1		ENGLAND/SCOTLAND/WALES	1
	18 - 19	2		IRELAND	2
	20 - 21	3		PAKISTAN/INDIA	3
	22 - 24	4		CHINA/JAPAN	4
	25 - 27	5		WEST INDIES	5
	28 - 30	6		AFRICA	6
	31+	7	OTHER (State)		7

BEFORE THE PANEL BABY WAS BORN:		(25)	INTERVIEWER: PLEASE INDICATE BELOW THE RACE OF THE RESPONDENT IF APPARENTLY DIFFERENT FROM THE PLACE OF BIRTH.		(34)
	WORKED FULL TIME	1		BRITISH	1
	WORKED PART TIME	2		PAKISTANI/INDIAN	2
	NO PAID JOB	3		CHINESE/JAPANESE	3
NOW :		(26)		OTHER ASIAN	4
	WORKING FULL TIME	1		WEST INDIAN/AFRICAN	5
	WORKING PART TIME	2	OTHER (State)		
	NO PAID JOB	3			

IF NOT WORKING Do you intend to go (back) to work in the next 2 years?		(27)
	YES FULL TIME	1
	YES PART TIME	2
	NO	3
	DON'T KNOW	4

P.T.O.

115

	CODE	ROUTE
Q.1 Where was your baby born? (IF HOSPITAL, ENTER NAME /ADDRESS) FULL NAME AND ADDRESS: HOSPITAL	(35) 1	Q.2
	(36)	
HOME/OTHER	A	Q.5
Q.2 During your stay in <u>hospital</u> after (panel baby's name) was born, did you feed him/her by breast only, bottle baby milk only or both?	(37)	
BREAST ONLY	1	Q.3
BOTTLE ONLY	2	Q.4
BREAST AND BOTTLE	3	
OTHER ANSWER	4	Q.5
Q.3 Even though you didn't bottle-feed in hospital, can you tell me the brand of milk that was available for bottle-feeders? DO <u>NOT</u> PROMPT	(38)	
CODE 1ST MENTION IF MORE THAN ONE AVAILABLE		
COW & GATE	1	
OSTERMILK (FARLEYS)	2	
SMA (WYETH)	3	Q.5
MILUMIL (MILUPA)	4	
OTHER/D.K.	5	
Q.4 Thinking back to the very first bottle feeds you gave in hospital, can you tell me the brand of milk you used at that time? DO <u>NOT</u> PROMPT	(39)	
COW & GATE	1	
OSTERMILK (FARLEYS)	2	
SMA (WYETH)	3	Q.5
MILUMIL (MILUPA)	4	
OTHER/D.K.	5	
Q.5a And are you <u>now</u> feeding him/her by breast milk only, bottle baby milk only or both?	(40)	
BREAST ONLY	1	
BOTTLE ONLY	2	Q.5b
BREAST AND BOTTLE	3	
Q.5b And is your baby taking any solids?		
SOLIDS	4	
NO SOLIDS	N	Q.6a

SHOW GIFT PARCEL PHOTOGRAPH

Q.6a Before or after (panel baby's name) was born, were you sent, given or did you buy any of these parcels of baby goods?

INTERVIEWER: CHECK FULL TITLE OF PARCEL(S) RECEIVED, TO MAKE SURE CORRECT ONE(S) RECORDED

FOR EACH PARCEL RECEIVED, ASK:

Q.6b Where did you get the parcel?

	THE BOUNTY BAG FOR A NEW MOTHER (FIRST BABY)	THE BOUNTY BAG FOR A MOTHER WITH OTHER CHILDREN	THE BOUNTY MOTHER-TO-BE SAMPLING SERVICE (PRE-NATAL)	ROUTE
Q.6a RECEIVED (41)	1	2	3	
Q.6b	(42)	(43)	(44)	
BY POST	1	1	1	
HOSPITAL	2	2	2	
CLINIC	3	3	3	SEE Q.7a
BOOTS	4	4	4	
OTHER	5	5	5	

ASK MOTHERS, WHOSE PANEL BABY IS A SUBSEQUENT BABY. OTHERS SEE BELOW

Q.7a Now I would like you to think back to your <u>previous</u> baby/babies and about the things you had.
For each item that I mention, please tell me whether you had one, for your previous baby/babies.

FOR EACH ITEM OWNED, ASK:

Q.7b And do you still have the <u>same</u> .... (item) as you had then?

	Q.7a HAD BEFORE	Q.7b STILL HAVE	
	(45)	(46)	
PUSH-CHAIR	1	1	
PLAYPEN	2	2	
TERRY NAPPIES	3	3	SEE BELOW
BABY BATH	4	4	
CARRICOT	5	5	

PUNCHER: SKIP 47 - 75

INTERVIEWER: OBTAIN MOTHER'S SIGNATURE, THEN SIGN YOURSELF AND ENTER YOUR INTERVIEWER NUMBER AND THE DATE

I CONFIRM MY AGREEMENT TO BECOME A MEMBER OF THE RSGB BABY PANEL

_____ (MOTHER'S SIGNATURE)

I HAVE EXPLAINED THE PANEL TO THIS MOTHER AND I AM SATISFIED SHE IS WILLING TO TAKE PART

(76)	(77)	(78)	(79)	(80)

_____ (INTERVIEWER'S SIGNATURE)

DATE: _____ (INTERVIEWER NUMBER) ——————▶

116

APPENDIX V Estimation of breast milk consumption

For this survey the volume of breast milk consumed was not measured directly. However, mothers were asked to record the number of feeds and the duration of feeding (excluding, for example, any time when the infant slept at the breast). Typical volumes of breast milk for full feeds were estimated from MRC data (Paul et al., 1988) to be approximately 135g for infants aged 6–7 months and 100g for those aged 8–12 months. We have assumed that a feed of 10 minutes or longer was equivalent to a full feed. For feeds of less than 10 minutes duration, weights have been calculated proportionally. Thus a five minute feed for an eight month old infant has been assumed to provide 50g of breast milk.

This approach may underestimate the intake of some infants and overestimate the intake of others. This potential source of error should be noted when considering the nutrient intake of breastfed infants.

Wastage

It was recognised that infants often do not consume all the food or drink offered to them. Interviewers therefore stressed the need to record what was actually eaten rather than the amount offered. In certain sections of the diary an additional column was left for 'amount eaten'.

Discrete items of food which were left or for example dropped could be relatively easily quantified, however infants are often messy eaters with food smeared on the face, hands and bibs. This wastage is difficult to quantify but is likely to be greatest at the beginning of the weaning process and again when infants start to feed themselves with a spoon. For most infants in the survey weaning was well established. Less than 20% of the sample were able to feed themselves with a spoon.

We concluded that for most infants the non-quantified food on hands, faces and bibs etc was likely to be nutritionally insignificant. Therefore, no further deductions have been made.

Nutrient databank

Intakes of nutrients were calculated from the records of food consumption using a specially developed nutrient databank. Past dietary surveys have largely relied upon the standard UK food composition tables, McCance and Widdowson's The Composition of Foods (Paul and Southgate, 1978). However, the composition of foods changes over time—not only are new products constantly being developed and old ones reformulated, but apparently traditional foods also change. Changes in the composition may result from, among other things, new plant varieties and animal breeds, importation from different countries, altered storage practices, processing techniques, fortification practices, packaging and domestic practices. Furthermore these tables do not contain information on commercial infant foods which are important sources of nutrients in the diets of young children. Since accepting responsibility for revision and extension of the UK food composition tables in 1978, MAFF has conducted a major programme of nutrient analyses in foods. Among these was an analytical survey of the nutritional content of a wide range of grouped samples of commercial infant food currently available in the UK. Although several commercial infant food manufacturers provided nutritional information on their products there are limitations to the data.

- the range of nutrient data is limited with few data available on the content of individual sugars, dietary fibre, fatty acids, and certain minerals and vitamins.

- vitamin and mineral information is frequently 'the amount added', or a minimum value rather than an actual value. Manufacturers often add considerably more to their product in order to safeguard possible losses particularly vitamins during the distribution process and ensure minimum levels reach the consumer.

Retail samples of the major commercial infant foods were purchased between 1985 and 1986 and analysed at the IFR Reading.

Methods of preparation Values for each nutrient in the databank which was included in the fourth edition of McCance and Widdowson's The Composition of Foods (Paul and Southgate, 1978) and Immigrant Foods (Tan et al., 1985), were evaluated and where they were considered still to be valid or where no other reliable data existed, these were used in the databank. These data were extended using the results of recent analytical surveys, manufacturers' data, published scientific literature and, where appropriate, food composition tables from other countries. For some foods no reliable information was available for certain nutrients. These values have not been taken as zero, but a likely value has been calculated from ingredients or imputed from similar foods.

Composite dishes and recipe calculations

In this survey when casseroles or stews were consumed in which either meat, fish and poultry was the main ingredient the mother was asked to indicate which vegetables it contained. Despite knowing the main ingredients, recipes of a particular dish will vary in the proportions of each constituent. Therefore, after a series of cooking experiments a standard recipe was devised for each type of casserole with particular vegetable combinations. The recipes included more water than the conventional recipes in order to take account of the likely consistency of pureed or chopped foods.

The nutrient content of composite dishes was calculated from the raw ingredients after allowing for likely moisture losses or gains and after making standard adjustments for nutrient losses on cooking (Paul and Southgate, 1978).

Details of nutrients measured

The nutrient data bank was constructed during 1987. Intakes were calculated for the following:

Moisture	(g)	
Sugars	(g)	total sugars, expressed as monosaccharide equivalents
Starch	(g)	expressed as monosaccharide equivalents
Dietary fibre	(g)	expressed as (non-starch polysaccharides Englyst method)
Energy	(kcal)	(4 × protein) + (9 × fat) + (3.75 × carbohydrate) + (7 × alcohol)
	(kJ)	(17 × protein) + (37 × fat) + (16 × carbohydrate) + (29 × alcohol)

Proximates

Protein	(g)	
Fat	(g)	
Carbohydrate	(g)	sum of sugars plus starch, expressed as monosaccharide equivalents

Inorganics

Sodium	(mg)
Potassium	(mg)
Calcium	(mg)
Magnesium	(mg)
Phosphorus	(mg)
Chloride	(mg)

Trace nutrients

Iron	(mg)
Copper	(mg)
Zinc	(mg)
Iodine	(µg)
Manganese	(mg)

Vitamins

Retinol	(µg)	sum of trans retinol + (0.75 × cis retinol) + (0.9 × retinaldehyde) + (0.4 × dehydroretinol)
Retinol equivalent	(µg)	$\text{retinol} + \dfrac{\beta\text{-carotene}}{6}$
Carotene	(µg)	largely as β-carotene
Vitamin D	(µg)	sum of cholecalciferol and ergocalciferol
Vitamin E	(mg)	tocopherol + (0.3 × tocopherol) + (0.15 × tocopherol) + (0.3 × tocotrienol)
Thiamin	(mg)	
Riboflavin	(mg)	
Niacin	(mg)	
Niacin equivalent	(mg)	(calculation niacin + tryptophan/60)
Vitamin B_6	(mg)	
Vitamin B_{12}	(µg)	
Folate	(µg)	
Pantothenic acid	(mg)	
Biotin	(µg)	
Vitamin C	(mg)	

Fatty acids

Saturates	(g)
Monounsaturates	(g)
Polyunsaturates	(g)
Cholesterol	(mg)

Individual sugars

Glucose	(g)	
Fructose	(g)	
Sucrose	(g)	expressed as monosaccharide
Maltose	(g)	expressed as monosaccharide
Lactose	(g)	expressed as monosaccharide
Others, dextrins	(g)	expressed as monosaccharide

Food groups

'Family foods'
- Pasta, rice
- Breakfast cereals
- Bread
- Biscuits and crispbreads
- Cakes, buns and puddings
- Milk, beverages made from milk
- Ice creams and creams
- Yogurt
- Cheeses and cheese dishes and pizza
- Egg and egg dishes
- Fat spreads
- Meat, meat dishes and meat products
- Offal and offal dishes
- Poultry and poultry dishes
- Fish and fish products
- Vegetables excluding potatoes
- Potatoes
- Fruits
- Nuts and nut spreads
- Preserves, chocolate spreads and fruit curds
- Chocolate confectionery
- Sugar confectionery
- Crisps and savoury snacks
- Fruit juice
- Tea and coffee (mostly water and a little milk)
- Soft drinks including squashes
- Water
- Miscellaneous food (gravies, soups, sauces, powdered drinks e.g. cocoa (recorded as dried weight))

Infant foods
- Manufactured baby foods in tins/jars
- Manufactured baby foods—dried/instant
- Rusks
- Milk formulas
- Baby juices and drinks
- Breast milk

APPENDIX IX # Broad classification of foods for nutrient analysis

Cereals	pasta, rice, bread, cakes, buns and puddings, biscuits and crispbreads, breakfast cereals
Milk and products	all cows milk and other milks (except infant milk formulas and breast milk), cheese and cheese dishes, yogurt, creams and ice-creams, beverages made with milk
Egg and egg dishes	
Fat spreads	butter, margarine and reduced fat and low fat spreads
Meat, meat products and dishes	meat, poultry, offal, meat products and dishes
Fish and fish products	fish, fish products and dishes
Vegetables	vegetables, potatoes and products including savoury snacks
Fruits and nuts	fruit, fruit products, nuts and nut products
Confectionery and preserves	chocolate and sugar confectionery, jam, marmalade
Beverages	tea, coffee, cocoa and drinking chocolate, branded drinks e.g. Horlicks all made with mostly water, soft drinks and squashes, fruit juices and alcoholic beverages
Miscellaneous	soups, gravies, pickles and sauces
Commercial Infant food	commercial infant food both jar, canned and instant or dried, rusks and infant fruit juices and drinks
Infant formulas	modified cows milk formulas, soy based formulas, follow-on milks
Breast milk	

Dietary Reference Values (DRVs) and their use in evaluating data from dietary surveys

The nutrient intakes of infants were compared with the Dietary Reference Values for Food Energy and Nutrients for the United Kingdom (DRVs) (DH, 1991) which replace the Recommended Daily Amounts (RDAs) (DHSS, 1979). The Panel on Dietary Reference Values, set up by the Committee on Medical Aspects of Food Policy (COMA), set a range of intakes based as far as possible on its assessment of the distribution of requirements for each nutrient. The Panel called these various figures Dietary Reference Values (DRVs).

The Panel considered that this change in approach and nomenclature would reduce the chance of misunderstanding the true nature of its figures as estimates of reference values and not as recommendations (misinterpreted to mean the minimum desired for a healthy diet) for intake by individuals or groups.

The Panel assumed that the distribution of requirements in a group of individuals for a nutrient is normally distributed. This gives a notional mean requirement or Estimated Average Requirement (EAR) of a group of people for energy or protein or a vitamin or mineral. About half will usually need more than the EAR, and half less (DH, 1991).

1.   The Reference Nutrient Intake (RNI) for protein or a vitamin or mineral is defined as two notional standard deviations above the EAR. The RNI is therefore an amount of the nutrient that is enough, or more than enough, for about 97% of people in a group. Intakes above this amount will certainly be adequate. If the average intake of a group is at the RNI, then the risk of deficiency in the group is very small (DH, 1991).

2.   The Lower Reference Nutrient Intake (LRNI) is defined as two notional standard deviations below the estimated average requirement. The LRNI represents the lowest intakes which will meet the needs of some individuals in the group. Intakes below this level are almost certainly inadequate for most individuals.

Interpretation of Dietary Reference Values

For most nutrients the Panel found insufficient data to establish any of the DRVs with great confidence. Uncertainties relating to the appropriate parameter by which to assess the requirement, to the completeness of the database for any nutrient, and to the precision and accuracy of dietary intake data lead to the need to make judgements (DH, 1991). Equally, when nutrient intakes are measured there is demonstrable inter-individual variation, which is not necessarily related to the variation in requirements. The time course of the relationship between intake and status varies between different nutrients. For instance daily energy intakes should approximate requirements while assessments of intakes of some micro-nutrients need to be integrated over days, weeks or even longer (DH, 1991).

The Dietary Reference Values apply to groups of healthy people. The RNI for any one nutrient presupposes that requirements for energy and all the other nutrients are met.

Uses of Dietary Reference Values for assessing diets of groups of individuals

When measures of individual diets are aggregated, intra-individual day to day variability is attenuated. Assuming that the inter-individual variability is random, then in a sufficiently large group, this source of imprecision is also diminished. Thus the group mean intake will more precisely represent the habitual group mean intake than any of the individual measures will represent habitual individual intakes.

If the dietary data are robust enough, it may be possible to say that 'X' per cent of the group had intakes below the RNI. If X is zero then the risk of deficiency in the whole group is extremely small. As X increases further so the risk of deficiency in the group increases.

Glossary of terms and abbreviations

Infant	Child who has not attained the age of one year
'Family foods'	All foods other than commercial infant foods, infant formulas and milk
'Commercial infant foods'	Foods, besides milk, manufactured primarily for infants in which the consistency and composition is suitable for this age
Stage I (as defined by manufacturers)	Smooth, mild flavoured first weaning foods for babies from about 3 months of age
Stage II (as defined by manufacturers)	Contain pieces of food to encourage an older baby of about 7 months to chew
Commercial infant puddings	Includes fruit based desserts and pure fruits
Infant fruit juices	Includes baby syrups (since been withdrawn), concentrated fruit juice drinks and ready to drink juice drinks manufactured primarily for infants
RDA	Recommended Daily Amount
RDA for nutrients	Average amount of the nutrient which should be provided per head in a group of people if the needs of practically all the members of the group are to be met
Dietary Reference Value (DRV)	A term used to cover LRNI, EAR, RNI and safe intake
EAR	Estimated Average Requirement of a group of people for energy or protein or a vitamin or mineral. About half will usually need more than the EAR, and half less.
LRNI	Lower Reference Nutrient Intake for protein or a vitamin or mineral. An amount of the nutrient that is enough for only the few people in a group who have low needs.
RNI	Reference Nutrient Intake for protein or a vitamin or mineral. An amount of the nutrient that is enough, or more than enough, for about 97% of people in a group. If average intake of a group is at RNI, then the risk of deficiency in the group is very small.
Children's vitamin drops	Vitamin supplements available through the welfare scheme, recommended by the DH from 6 months
Mothers	Broad term used to describe mothers and carers of infant
Incidence of breastfeeding	Proportion of babies who were breastfed initially
Typical portion size	Average quantity of a specified food or food group eaten by the infant at any one time

Intrinsic sugars	Any sugar which is contained within the cell wall of the food
Extrinsic sugars	Any sugar which is not contained within cell walls e.g. sugars in fruit juice, honey, table sugar, and lactose in milk and milk products
Non-milk extrinsic sugars (NMES)	Extrinsic sugars except lactose in milk and milk products
Non-starch polysaccharides (NSP)	A precisely measurable component of foods. The best measure of dietary fibre
Socioeconomic group —ABC1 —C2DE	Grouped according to the occupation of the head of household
MAFF	Ministry of Agriculture, Fisheries and Food
Quantiles	The quantiles of a distribution divide it into two equal parts. The Median of a distribution divides it into two equal parts, such that there are equal numbers of values above and below the median.
Median	see Quantiles
DH	Department of Health
DHSS	Department of Health and Social Security

Printed in the United Kingdom for HMSO
Dd294826 11/92 C15 G531 10170